5 29
J1

Cooking for Health

DIABETES and HYPOGLYCEMIA

Macrobiotic Food and Cooking Series

Cooking for Health

Diabetes
and
Hypoglycemia

by Aveline Kushi

edited by Rosalind Rhodes

foreword by Lawrence H. Kushi, Sc.D.

Japan Publications, Inc.
Tokyo • New York

Note to the reader: Those with health problems are advised to seek the guidance
of a qualified medical, or psychological professional in addition to qualified
macrobiotic counselor before implementing any of the dietary and other approaches presented in this book. It is essential that any reader who has any
reason to suspect serious illness in themselves or their family members seek
appropriate medical, nutritional, or psychological advice promptly. Neither this
or any other health related book should be used as a substitute for qualified
care or treatment.

Published by JAPAN PUBLICATIONS, INC., Tokyo and New York

Distributors:
UNITED STATES: *Kodansha International/USA, Ltd., through Farrar, Straus &
Giroux, 19 Union Square West, New York, 10003.* CANADA: *Fitzhenry & Whiteside
Ltd., 195 Allstate Parkway, Markham, Ontario, L3R 4T8.* BRITISH ISLES: *Premier
Book Marketing Ltd., 1 Gower Street, London WC1E 6HA.* EUROPEAN CONTINENT:
European Book Service PBD, Strijkviertel 63, 3454 PK De Meern, The Netherlands.
AUSTRALIA AND NEW ZEALAND: *Bookwise International, 54 Crittenden Road,
Findon, South Australia 5007.* THE FAR EAST AND JAPAN: *Japan Publications
Trading Co., Ltd., 1–2–1, Sarugaku-cho, Chiyoda-ku, Tokyo 101.*

First edition: April 1985
Third printing: September 1989

LCCC No. 84–081361
ISBN 0–87040–617–5

Printed in U.S.A.

Foreword━━━━━━━━━━━━━━━━━━━━━━━━━━

It is a paradox of modern medicine that chronic diseases have become commonplace even as their underlying physiology and pathology become better understood and new technologies to combat them are put into use. One needs only to examine the natural history and epidemiology of chronic diseases to observe that this is so: The occurrence of chronic diseases increases, often dramatically, with the Westernization of traditional cultures.

Against this background, it is not surprising that more attention is being directed at lifestyle factors that may influence the development or progression of disease. For example, diet has been an important component of the management of diabetes mellitus, since impaired insuline metabolism is known to be a primary problem associated with diabetes. However, until recently the cornerstone of dietary management was restriction of dietary carbohydrates. The basis for this was the belief that fluctuations in insulin need are directly related to total carbohydrate intake. More recently, in the past 10 to 15 years, dietary recommendations for the management of diabetes have included an increase in dietary complex carbohydrates including fiber, and a decrease in simple carbohydrates such as sugar. Thus, quality of carbohydrates in the diet is now recognized to be as important as quantity. An added benefit of such a diet, being relatively low in fat and cholesterol, is that it could decrease the chances of developing heart disease.

The change in dietary recommendations for diabetes has paralleled the growing public awareness concerning diet and nutrition in general. The current recommendations were also anticipated in large part by macrobiotics, the guidelines of which promotes a dietary pattern that emphasizes whole grains, beans, fresh vegetables and fruits. Indeed, one of the most striking aspects of sound dietary guidelines, whether based primarily on philosophical or scientific grounds, is the degree of agreement among them. The accord between current American Diabetes Association dietary guidelines and macrobiotic dietary guidelines, properly adapted for diabetes prevention or management, is an example of this.

The guidelines and recipes within the pages of this book are based on macrobiotic principles. They can be of benefit to all people, not just in the management and prevention of diabetes, if adopted with common sense and a spirit of adventure. Some of the bases put forth for the guidelines presented here may seem without scientific merit. This should not prevent the open-minded exploration of the benefits and risks of adopting such dietary guidelines. With a properly informed perspective, this book can be the first practical step toward a healthier lifestyle.

LAWRENCE HARUO KUSHI, SC. D.
January, 1985

Acknowledgments

I would like to thank Japan Publications, Inc. for the opportunity to write this book and for their patience in waiting for its completion.

Thanks to Edward and Wendy Esko and Olivia Oredson for some preliminary research, outline and business arrangements.

Thanks to Rosalind Rhodes for co-writing the book.

Thanks to John D. Mann for overseeing the project, editing and contributing the chapters, *Understanding Diabetes and Hypoglycemia* and *Dietary Adjustments for Diabetes and Hypoglycemia*.

Thanks to Onike Breedy for editing the chapter, *The Underlying Cosmology*. Thanks to Evelyne Harboun for proofreading and editing the recipes.

Thanks to Michio Kushi for writing the companion book, *Diabetes and Hypoglycemia (Macrobiotic Health Education Series)* as well as offering permission to use his notes on the Standard Macrobiotic Diet and some diagrams for his other books. Thanks to John D. Mann for helping him write the book.

Thanks to Lily Kushi for the illustrations.

Also, thanks to Lawrence H. Kushi, Phillip Y. Kushi, Ann Rawley, Shigeko Ando, Mayumi Nishimura and Steve and Carolyn Gagne for extra comments, suggestions and recipes.

Contents

10

Introduction

Having sugars and sweets in our diet is very important. Among the five categories of tastes—sweet, salty, sour, pungent and bitter—the sweet taste is the most central and should comprise 60 to 70 percent of our intake. The other tastes are just as important but quantity-wise they should be much smaller. There are many types of sweets. For most balance and health, the best quality sugars are contained in whole grains, sweet vegetables (carrots, onions, cabbage, parsnips, squash, broccoli and so on) as well as from occasional fruits—more complex sugar than simple sugar.

Problems like diabetes and hypoglycemia come from using white refined sugar. By substituting sweet grains and vegetables there will be no side-effects and though good quality food is sometimes more expensive, the total expense of life-style is much less.

It may take awhile to adjust to a more balanced diet and many strong cravings for white sugar may arise. Pay close attention to what you eat daily and use barley malt, rice syrup, and other sources of complex sugar to help satisfy your cravings. I hope this book can help you as a guide.

1. The Underlying Cosmology▬▬▬▬▬▬

There is a vast cosmology behind the principles of macrobiotics, a cosmology which sets out to explain the creation and the interrelationship of all phenomena throughout the universe to which we are a part.

The real purpose of macrobiotics is to empower us with the ability to fulfill our potentials and dreams and to serve as a reminder that we are the builders and masters of our own lives.

Macrobiotics is a rich and unlimited field of study that extends far beyond the scope of this book which you may feel free to pursue. In doing so, you will become your own guide, discovering for yourself what you need to do to maintain your health and to accomplish your personal goals. In this chapter is a brief overview of the underlying philosophy on which macrobiotics is based and how it applies to the aspects of diet and health.

Everything in the universe is a constantly moving and changing energy varying in density and speed. Even seemingly stable and solid objects, for instance, a rock or a table, are made up of moving molecules, atoms, electrons and protons which themselves are nothing but energy.

The origin and destination of all phenomena is Infinity, also called God, the Universal Will, the Super Consciousness or Nothingness. There is no time or space, past or future, light or darkness here. There is only endless motion, moving at an infinite speed in all directions.

These currents of endless motion (refer to Fig. 1) intersect and create logarithmic spirals which spin inwards towards the center in a contracting, centripetal (also referred to as the *yang* force) direction and opposite logarithmic spirals which spin outwards from the center in an expanding, centrifugal (also referred to as the *yin* force) direction. The formation of these spirals is how everything comes into being. In fact, these opposite but complimentary forces, by their constant interaction, are creating all things material and non-material. The Figure below shows the "Eternal and Universal Cycle of Change" reprinted from the *Book of Dō-In: Exercise for Physical and Spiritual Development* by Michio Kushi, (p. 18).

When moving in a yang (△) direction, the energy begins to take on more and more form in a process of materialization. Generally speaking, this process can be characterized by increasing speed, increasing temperature, and more density and weight which manifests as smallness or contraction, more material, hotter, faster, heavier and smaller. When moving in a yin (▽) direction energy takes on the opposite characteristics. It is less formed, more diffused, expanded, more cold, slower, and lighter. Yang

14

Fig. 1 The Eternal and Universal Cycle of Change.

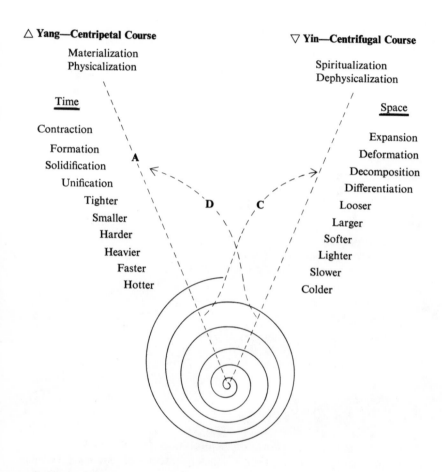

△ Yang—Centripetal Course

Materialization
Physicalization

Time

Contraction
Formation
Solidification
Unification
Tighter
Smaller
Harder
Heavier
Faster
Hotter

A

D   C

▽ Yin—Centrifugal Course

Spiritualization
Dephysicalization

Space

Expansion
Deformation
Decomposition
Differentiation
Looser
Larger
Softer
Lighter
Slower
Colder

motion is followed by yin, and yin motion is followed by yang. Yang does not exist without yin and vice versa.

All phenomena are created from these two opposite forces or directions of yin and yang which grew out of what we call God, Infinity, and so on. The spiral below is an illustration of the "Creation of the Universe." (Reprinted from the *Book of Dō-In: Exercise for Physical and Spiritual Development* by Michio Kushi, p. 23.)

15

Fig. 2   The Creation of the Universe.

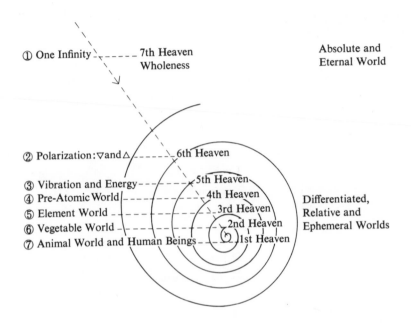

① *One Infinity*:   Absolute and eternal, nothing but infinite motion.
② *Polarization—Yin (▽) and Yang (△)*:   The beginning of time and space, direction, dimensions, relativity, differentiation, and the ephemeral world.
③ *Vibration and Energy*:   The beginning of light, sound, long and short waves, the subconscious and conscious mind, mental and spiritual phenomena.
④ *Pre-Atomic World*:   The world of electrons, neutrons and other pre-atomic particles and the beginning of the material world.
⑤ *Element World*:   The world of molecules, the elements (hydrogen, helium, etc.), soil, water, air, fire, our senses and the beginning of the visible world.
⑥ *Vegetable World*:   The plant kingdom.
⑦ *Animal World and Human Beings*:   The animal kingdom including human beings.

16

Human beings, as the end result of a yang, centripetal spiral, are also at the beginning of a yin, centrifugal spiral. As we develop in a more yang direction we are created by physical food, the elemental energies from the sun, water, wind and so on, and the vibrations of thoughts from the mind. After we are formed in the physical world as we know it we start to go in the opposite yin direction as we develop emotionally, mentally and spiritually, and our body eventually decomposes and our soul later melts back into the infinite void.

The Figure below shows the "Eternal Cycle of Life." (Reprinted from the *Book of Dō-In: Exercise for Physical and Spiritual Development.* by Michio Kushi, p. 33.)

Fig. 3   The Eternal Cycle of Life.

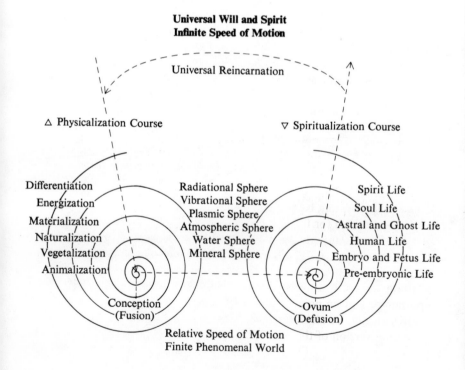

Universal Will and Spirit
Infinite Speed of Motion

Universal Reincarnation

△ Physicalization Course   ▽ Spiritualization Course

Differentiation	Radiational Sphere	Spirit Life
Energization	Vibrational Sphere	Soul Life
Materialization	Plasmic Sphere	Astral and Ghost Life
Naturalization	Atmospheric Sphere	Human Life
Vegetalization	Water Sphere	Embryo and Fetus Life
Animalization	Mineral Sphere	Pre-embryonic Life

Conception
(Fusion)

Ovum
(Defusion)

Relative Speed of Motion
Finite Phenomenal World

As you can see, the most contracted or yang point, the fusion of sperm and egg, is immediately followed by the yin, expanding force of rapid growth. (Yang in the extreme or at its peak turns into yin and vice versa.) This is followed by pre-embryonic life, which is followed by the watery and totally dark world of the embryo and fetus, followed by the airy atmosphere of our human environment as we know it. This world of air is half in darkness and half in light. When we pass away we shed our physical body and enter the plasmic astral world of ghosts or spiritual phenomena which is totally immersed in light. Each of the above successive worlds becomes more expansive, freer and involves a longer so-called time span.

By maintaining a healthy mind, body and spirit we are able to move more smoothly and happily into the next world. A pregnant woman has been traditionally told to get proper and balanced nourishment, sufficient exercise and rest, and to avoid violence in pastimes—movies, books and the like. She is also advised to send happy and beautiful thoughts to the baby so that the infant can come into this world in a healthy, happy state. In this way the child can live more peacefully and unencumbered. Likewise, in this life, we can all consider the quality of the various types of food we receive, the kinds of exercise and physical activity and rest we take, and encourage positive, creative thoughts and actions so that our birth into the next world will be smooth and our life there will be enjoyable. The spirits of unhappy persons are full of sorrow and delusion and instead of moving forward and onward into a brighter freer world of light, they remain attached to the earthly level and to the people and places they knew. The Oriental and other "primitive" cultures send their consolation, love, and wishes of happiness to their deceased ancestors. This helps to free these spirits and assists their ascent onto a broader and more joyful plane of existence.

We are all traveling back towards the outer parts of the universal spiral of life as we search for freedom, peace of mind, happiness, the ability to spread our wings and finally to be one with God. Even those who seemingly only want money or material possessions are actually looking for this same happiness and freedom and they feel it will result from their material pursuits. It is proper that each person pursues what he feels important at a given point. This is our freedom.

Paradoxically, we already are where we want to be as we ourselves are a miniature version of the whole universe at the same time that we are our small individual selves. Deep inside, each of us knows somehow that there is a larger I or self, a part of us which is eternal, all knowing and subject to no boundaries. There is a more synchronized feeling of unity, oneness and connection between our smaller I, our human existence, and our bigger I, this infinite universe, when we are in a relaxed, healthy, vibrant, in tune with nature state. We can tap into the unlimited, creative potential that we have in the universe and use it to direct our life with much more awareness when we are in harmonious synchronicity.

The deeper meaning of health is being in this aligned and synchronous state which results in a smooth, unblocked, effortless flow of our energies between all the inner and outer universal parts of ourselves. The macrobiotic approach to well-being is a holistic approach directed by our understanding that a change in any aspect or portion of our body or self has an effect on everything else including the world and the universe. There are several approaches one can take to create a free flow of energy:

1. *Changing your diet:* This is the perspective that this book basically focuses on. What we eat creates our blood cells, and hence the formation of our organs and all other parts of our body. It is a wonder that food is not often associated as a major cause of disease. One's diet also alters the mind and emotions. We know that the ingestion of alcohol and various licit and illicit drugs effects one's mental state. This fact cannot be argued. Likewise, anything else one takes in has its effect on our being, though it may be on a subtle level.

2. *Working with the powers of the mind:* Everything that exists has its origin in the invisible world of the mind and vibrations. It is said that what we believe manifests. There are many negative thoughts or assumptions that we may dwell on which can influence our lives. Many of these delusions, as we may call them here, occur automatically and unconsciously. One may develop self-awareness by constantly observing the thoughts, actions, and reactions that control one's life and rechannel unwanted habits into more positive ideas and dreams.

3. *Relaxation:* Mental and physical tension block the freest flow of energy. A technique one may try is to take an inventory of all the parts of your body and relax all tense spots. You can do the same thing with the mind, letting go of anxiety, guilt and anger. Use the breath to help the relaxation process: breathe slowly and deeply.

4. *Palm-healing, shiatsu massage, moxibustion, acupuncture and chiropractics:* These practices can be used to temporarily unblock stagnations of energy in the body.

5. *Keep mentally and physically active:* Exercise, do sports or dancing, clean your house, garden, read, study, engage in hobbies, draw, write,

compose, play music, do volunteer work, teach . . . whatever you want. Make sure to do both mental and physical work. The more energy we circulate, the more comes back to us and the less stagnation there is in our lives.

6. *Changing ones environmental surroundings:* In some cases, it might be necessary to change ones environmental surroundings. Some forms of sicknesses can be more easily eliminated in a warm climate while others may require cooler temperatures. Moving to a quieter locale, like the countryside may be beneficial for some conditions. Also, it's important that one be in a loving atmosphere with people who care about you and give you support. Also, one can help to maintain a clean, unpolluted, ecologically balanced world by using biodegradable materials as much as possible, not taking more than one needs, as well as helping to protect the well-being of our fellow inhabitants on this earth—the members of the plant and animal kingdoms.

7. *Maintain good relationships with all the people in your life:* Blaming, holding grudges, anger, fear and hatred makes one very tense and causes blockages. We create the circumstances of our individual lives so it is up to us to change them. Give everyone your love, support, and respect for their freedom and individuality.

8. *Be grateful and thankful for all that you have been given:* Notice all the beauty and marvels in the world. Look at any hardships, difficulties, or rejections you encounter as opportunities for self-reflection and growth.

Working on just one of the above recommendations can be tremendously helpful and have a positive effect on us overall but to make a really permanent and thorough change for the better, all of the above should be worked on as they are interrelated. Many people form an exclusive allegiance to one approach and as time passes they wonder why their plans and dreams don't progress beyond a certain point. They then abandon their one approach and either give up or make an exclusive attachment to another approach. Please beware of this tendency.

Yin and Yang

Everything is created and governed by the interactions of yin and yang, the two opposite poles which are endlessly manifesting in the world. Below is a chart of some classification examples:

Attribute	Yin/Centrifugal (▽)	Yang/Centripetal (△)
Tendency	Expansion	Contraction
Function	Dispersion, decomposition	Assimilation, organization
Movement	More inactive, slower	More active, faster
Vibration	Shorter waves, high frequency	Longer waves, low frequency
Direction	Vertical; ascending	Horizontal, descending
Position	More outward and peripheral	More inward and central
Weight	Lighter	Heavier
Temperature	Colder	Hotter
Light	Darker	Lighter
Humidity	More wet	More dry
Density	Thinner	Thicker
Size	Larger	Smaller
Shape	More expanded, fragile	More contracted, harder
Length	Longer	Shorter
Texture	Softer	Harder
Atomic particle	Electron	Proton
Elements	N, O, K, P, Ca	H, C, Na, As, Mg
Environment	Vibration→Air→Water→	Earth
Climate	Tropical	Arctic
Biological	Vegetable	Animal
Sex	Female	Male
Organ structure	Hollow, expansive	Compact, condensed
Nerves	Orthosympathetic	Parasympathetic
Attitude	Gentle, negative	Active, positve
Work	Psychological & mental	Physical & social
Consciousness	More universal	More specific
Mental function	Dealing with the future	Dealing with the past
Culture	Spiritually oriented	Materially oriented
Color	Purple→Blue→Green→Yellow→	Brown→Orange→Red
Season	Winter	Summer
Dimension	Space	Time
Taste	Hot→sour→sweet→	Salty→Bitter
Vitamins	C	K, D
Catalyst	Water	Fire

By learning how yin and yang relate to each other you can begin to understand all the workings of the world. *I-Ching, The Book of Changes,* is based on yin-yang interactions. Macrobiotic dietary principles are drawn from this base.

Yin attracts yang and yang attracts yin, resulting in the harmony and marriage of two opposites. Examples are; man and woman, plus and minus magnets or electrical charges, electron and proton, spirit and matter, and so on. Upon injesting a quantity of salt (yang) for instance, one is then attracted to liquids (yin).

Yin repels yin, yang repels yang. Examples are: oil and water (both yin) don't mix. Two plus poles repel each other as do two minus poles.

The force of attraction (or repulsion as the case may be) is proportional to the ratio of the yin and yang elements. Their combination in various proportions creates an infinite variety of energies and phenomena where no two things in existence are identical.

Yin and yang are not static and are always flowing from one to another in various degrees. Yin in the extreme changes to yang and vice versa. Nothing lasts forever. Day turns into night, night into day. Activity is followed by rest, rest by activity. Success follows failure and failure follows success. Civilizations rise and fall. What has a beginning has an end.

Nothing is totally yin or totally yang. All things are made up of both. The more yin something is, the more yang it is as well. Many people that appear yang, strong, rough and tough on the outside may in comparison be yin, weak, and fragile on the inside. Others that appear yin, soft, and fragile on the outside may well be yang, strong and stubborn on the inside. Something that is structurally yang, as is the dense and compacted liver, is energetically yin; it functions without much motion. Things that are structurally yin, as a hollow heart, are energetically more yang, as it never stops pumping, contracting and expanding. The bigger the front, the bigger the back.

Large yin attracts small yin, large yang attracts small yang. After you take sugar (large yin) you are drawn to drinking more fluids (small yin).

Yin creates yang, yang creates yin. A yin, colder climate creates yang, small, hardy vegetation and a more yang, ambitious, hard-driving society. While a yang, warmer climate creates yin, watery, large, lush vegetation and a more slow paced, easy going and relaxed society.

Everything on this earth is created by varying proportions of upward and downward energies. Gravity is an example of downward energy. The growth of trees and plants is an example of upward energy.

Yin and Yang and Diet ────────────────────────

Yang foods give warmth, strength, discipline and vitality. Excessively yang foods (such as red meat, eggs or too much salt) are known to cause rigidity, egocentricity, exclusivity, constrictions, restlessness, arthritic conditions, heart attacks, violent tendencies and the like.

Yin foods are cooling, cleansing, relaxing and nurture patience and understanding. Excessively yin foods (such as honey, sugar, chemicals and drugs) have been shown to cause weakening and dispersion of the functioning capabilities in body and mind, including fear, defensiveness, loss of will, suspectibility to so-called viruses, a rampage of white blood cell production, and depression or suicidal tendencies, to name some common problems.

When taking in overly yang foods, one is automatically attracted to overly yin ones (and vice versa) to make balance and compensation. One may end up on a wild or chaotic seesaw with a combination of unwanted side-effects such as the ones listed above. Macrobiotics recommends a diet of more centrally balanced foods. Grains are the most centered and appropriate foods for human beings, requiring only a minimum amount of counterbalancing. (Grains are our complementary opposites as they are the last stage of plant evolution just as we are the last stage of animal evolution.) Brown rice, especially, has the right proportions of yin and yang for humans and provides the most stabilizing dietary staple.

Humans are constitutionally yang, warm-blooded beings and therefore require most if not all of their nourishment from their complementary opposite, which is the yin, vegetable kingdom. Among animal foods, fish is the recommended choice, particularly slow moving, white-meat varieties as well as some shellfish. The human digestive system doesn't digest or assimilate meat well. It lingers and putrefies in the stomach. The only circumstance where it is healthy to eat large amounts of animal food is in the very cold, yin, arctic regions where more strongly yang food is needed and where the availability of plant food is minimal.

Actually, climate plays a major role in our choice of available edibles. It is recommended that we choose fresh produce which is grown or can grow in our own climatic zone. Tropical fruits are more appropriate when consumed where they are grown but they are detrimental to one's health when taken in large quantities or too regularly in the temperate zone.

The seasons as well play an important part in food selection. For instance, in the spring when the energy is rising and expanding we should include fresh young greens and sprouts. Towards fall and then winter, when the energies are descending and contracting, squash, kale, and winter

23

Fig. 4   General Yin (▽) and Yang (△) Categorization of Food

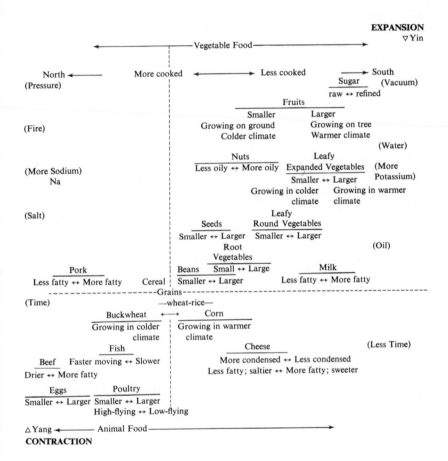

The above chart gives the general idea of the classification of food groups from yang to yin, from yin to yang. However, more precise classification should be made upon examination of environmental conditions, nature and structure, chemical compounds, and effect upon our physical and mental conditions. Also, cooking can greatly change food qualities from yin to yang and yang to yin.

storable vegetables such as root vegetables, and dried plants such as sea vegetables should be consumed.

A variety of cooking methods should be employed as well. In the winter, we can eat more well-cooked, slightly saltier, pressure-cooked, and baked foods as well as more fish. In the summer more lightly-cooked, boiled, raw (such as salads and fruit), chilled and steamed foods and desserts may be consumed.

Also, within one meal we should ideally have a representation of a variety of cooking styles as well as a variety of tastes, color and sizes.

Two additional factors which determine what is yin and what is yang and to what relative degree are: (1) rate of growth (faster is more yin and slower is more yang) and (2) portion of the plant being considered— whether roots (more yang) or leaves and fruits (more yin), and so on.

The preceding chart, from the *Book of Macrobiotics: The Universal Way of Health and Happiness* by Michio Kushi, p. 57, represents a general yin/yang categorization of foods.

2. Explanation of the Standard Macrobiotic Diet

These dietary recommendations are suggested for individuals in a general sound state of health. Persons having a more serious condition may need further modifications. It should also be noted that this is a general guideline and no matter what your condition, each person's individuality, lifestyle and environment need to be taken into account with the diet adapted accordingly.

To see exactly what foods are recommended, refer to the detailed food list following the section below on proportions.

1. WHOLE CEREAL GRAINS. It is recommended that at least 50% of every meal include cooked, organically grown, whole cereal grains prepared in a variety of ways.

2. SOUPS. Approximately 5–10% of your daily food intake (one or two bowls daily) may include soup made with traditional and naturally processed *miso* or *tamari* soy sauce. The flavor should not be overly salty, and your soup may include a variety of grains, beans and vegetables, including sea vegetables such as *wakame* and *kombu*.

3. VEGETABLES. About 20–30% of each meal may include local and organically grown vegetables with a large amount cooked in various styles and a smaller amount eaten as raw salad.

4. BEANS AND SEA VEGETABLES. Approximately 5–10% of your daily diet may include cooked beans and sea vegetables.

   Sea vegetables may be prepared in a variety of ways. They can be cooked with beans or vegetables, used in soups, or cooked and eaten separately as side dishes, flavored with a moderate amount of *tamari* soy sauce, sea salt, or rice vinegar.

5. SUPPLEMENTARY FOODS. Approximately 5–10%. Once or twice weekly a small amount of fresh white-meat fish may be eaten if desired.

   Fruit desserts, including fresh and dried fruits, may also be consumed on occasion. Local and organically grown fruits are preferred. Frequent use of fruit juice is not advisable. However, occasional consumption in warmer weather is allowable, depending on your health.

Lightly roasted seeds may be enjoyed as a snack. Though less frequently, some roasted nuts may be consumed. Rice syrup and barley malt may be used occasionally to add a sweet taste; rice vinegar or *umeboshi* vinegar may also be used occasionally for a sour taste.

6. BEVERAGES.   Any traditional tea which does not have an aromatic fragrance or a stimulant effect can be used such as *bancha* (*kukicha*) twig tea, and roasted grain teas. You may also drink a moderate amount of water (preferably spring or well water). Iced drinks are best avoided.

7. FOODS TO BE AVOIDED FOR BETTER HEALTH.   Meat, eggs, animal fat, poultry, dairy products, including butter, yogurt, ice cream, milk and cheese.

Tropical or semi-tropical fruits and fruit juices, soda, artificial drinks and beverages, coffee, colored tea, and all aromatic, stimulant teas such as mint and peppermint tea.

All artificially colored, preserved, sprayed, or chemically treated foods. All refined polished grains, flours and their derivatives. Mass-produced industrialized food including all canned and frozen foods.

Hot spices, any aromatic, stimulant food or food accessory; artificial vinegar and other seasonings. Licit and illicit drugs are best avoided. (Medicines prescribed by a physician do not apply to this general guideline.) Alcohol and cigarettes should be kept to a minimum.

8. ADDITIONAL SUGGESTIONS.   Cooking oil should be vegetable quality only. If you wish to improve your health use only cold-pressed mechanically expelled unrefined sesame or corn oil in moderate amounts.

Salt should be naturally processed sea salt and excessive use should be avoided. Traditional, non-chemicalized *tamari* or *shoyu* sauce and *miso* may also be used like sea salt.

You may eat regularly two to three times per day, as much as you want, provided the proportion is correct and chewing is thorough (at least 50 times per mouthful or until it becomes liquid). Please avoid eating for approximately three hours before sleeping.

A More Detailed Macrobiotic Food List ━━━━━

Items marked with an asterisk (*) are foods that may have to be avoided
or restricted when trying to cure some illnesses; look under the list of diet
modifications for specific diseases for more information.

Grains: ━━━━━

Regular use	Occasional use	Occasional flour products
Short grain brown rice	Long grain brown rice	Whole wheat noodles*
Medium grain brown rice	Sweet brown rice	Udon noodles*
Barley	*Mochi*	*Somen* noodles*
Pearl barley	Cracked wheat, bulghur	*Soba* noodles (buckwheat)*
Millet	Steel cut oats	
Corn	Rolled oats*	Unyeasted whole wheat bread*
Corn on the cob	Corn grits*	Unyeasted rye bread*
Whole oats	Corn meal*	*Fu**
Whole wheat berries	Rye Flakes	*Seitan**
Buckwheat*	Couscous	
Rye		

Vegetables: ━━━━━

Regular use	Occasional use	Avoid
Acorn squash	Celery*	Artichoke
Bok choy	Chives*	Bamboo shoots
Broccoli	Coltsfoot*	Beets
Brussels sprouts	Cucumber*	Curley dock
Burdock	Endive*	Eggplant
Butternut squash	Escarole*	Fennel
Cabbage	Green beans*	Ferns
Carrots & their tops	Green peas*	Ginseng
Cauliflower	Iceberg lettuce*	Green & red peppers
Chinese cabbage	Jerusalem artichoke*	New Zealand spinach
Collard greens	Kohlrabi*	Okra
Daikon & their tops	Lambsquarters*	Plantain
Dandelion roots, leaves	Mushrooms*	Purslane & sheperd's purse
Hubbard squash	Patty-pan squash*	Potato
Hokkaido pumpkin	Romaine lettuce*	Sorrel
Jinenjo	Salsify*	Spinach
Kale	*Shiitake* mushrooms*	Sweet potato
Leeks	Snap beans*	Swiss chard
Lotus root	Snow peas*	

Mustard greens
Onion
Parsley
Parsnip
Pumpkin
Radish
Red cabbage
Rutabaga
Scallions
Turnips & greens
Watercress

Sprouts*
Summer squash*
Wax beans*

Tomato
Taro potato (albi)
Yams
Zucchini

Beans:

Regular use	Occasional use	Occasional bean substitutes
Azuki beans	Black-eyed peas*	Dried *tofu*
Black soybeans	Black turtle beans*	Fresh *tofu**
Chickpeas (garbanzos)	Great northern beans*	*Natto**
Lentils (green)	Kidney beans*	*Tempeh**
	Lima beans*	
	Mung Beans*	
	Navy beans*	
	Pinto beans*	
	Soybeans*	
	Split peas*	
	Whole dried peas*	

Sea Vegetables:

All these sea vegetables can be used regularly. *Arame, Hijiki, Kombu,* toasted *Nori, Wakame,* Dulse, Agar-agar, Irish moss, *Mekabu.*

Fruits (usually cooked or dried):

Occasional use	Avoid
Apples*	Avocados
Apricots*	Bananas
Blueberries*	Coconuts
Blackberries*	Dates
Cantaloupes*	Figs
Cherries*	Grapefruit
Grapes*	Kiwi fruit
Lemons (small amounts of juice for cooking)*	Oranges
	Mangoes
Peaches*	Papayas

Pears*

Plums*

Raisins*

Raspberries*

Strawberries*

Watarmelon*

Persimmons

Pineapple

All other tropical fruits

Seeds and Nuts: ─────────────────────────────

Occasional use

Almonds*

Chestnuts*

Peanuts*

Pumpkin seeds*

Sesame seeds*

Sunflower seeds*

Walnuts*

Avoid

Brazil nuts

Caraway seeds

Cashews

Hazel nuts

Macadamian nuts

Pistachios

Poppy seeds

Spanish peanuts

All tropical nuts

Animal Foods and Their Products: ─────────────────

Occasional use

Carp*

Clams*

Cod*

Flounder*

Halibut*

Lobster*

Oysters*

Trout*

Red snapper*

Sole*

White-meat fish in general*

Avoid

Red-meat fish

Chicken

All fowl

Eggs

All mammals

All dairy products

Pickles: ─────────────────────────────────────

Regular use

Bran pickles

Brine pickles

Miso bran pickles

Miso pickles

Pressed pickles

Sauerkraut

Tamari Pickles

Takuan Pickles

Avoid

Commercial dill pickles

Herb pickles

Garlic pickles

Spiced pickles

Apple cider vinegar pickles

Wine vinegar pickles

Sweets:

Regular use	Occasional use	Avoid
Cabbage	Amazake*	All tropical fruits
Carrots	Barley malt*	Brown sugar
Daikon	Chestnuts*	Carob
Onions	See fruit list*	Chocolate
Parsnips	Hot apple cider*	Fructose
Pumpkin	Hot apple juice*	Honey
Squash	Rice malt syrup*	Maple syrup
		Molasses
		White sugar

Beverages:

Regular use	Occasional use	Infrequent use	Avoid
Bancha twig tea (Kukicha)	Grain coffee (100% grain)	Green tea*	Distilled water
		Vebetable juices*	Coffee
Bancha stem tea	Dandelion tea	Juices of fruits	Cold, iced drinks
Roasted barley tea	Kombu tea	from fruit list*	Hard liquor
Roasted brown rice tea	Umeboshi tea	Beer*	Herb teas
	Mu tea	Saké*	Mineral water & all bubbly water
Spring water			Regular tea
Well water			Stimulants
			Sugared drinks
			Tap water
			Whisky
			Wine

Seasonings and Oils:

Regular use	Occasional use	Avoid
Natural miso	Corn oil*	Animal fats
Dark sesame oil*	Ginger*	Butter & cream
Light sesame oil*	Horseradish*	Coconut oil
Natural soy sauce	Mirin*	Cottonseed oil
Tamari soy sauce	Olive oil*	Commercial dressings
Unrefined white sea salt	Rice vinegar*	Garlic
	Safflower oil*	Linseed oil
Umeboshi plum & paste	Sunflower oil*	Margarine
Umeboshi vinegar		Mayonnaise
		Commercial miso
		Mustard
		Pepper

Peanut oil
Table salt
All commercial season-
    ings
Soybean oil
Commercial soy sauce
All spices

Condiments:

Main condiments
Gomashio (sesame salt)
Sea vegetable powder
Sea vegetable powder with roasted
    sesame seeds
Tekka
Umeboshi plum

Other condiments
Brown rice vinegar
Cooked miso with scallions &
    onions
Nori condiment
Roasted sesame seeds
Shiso leaves & roasted sesame seeds
Shio Kombu
Umeboshi plum with raw scallions/
    onions
Umeboshi vinegar

Snacks:

You can have leftovers, noodles, popcorn (unbuttered), puffed whole
cereal grain, rice balls, rice cakes, roasted seeds, sushi, and whole wheat
bread.

Cooking and Preparation Methods:

Regular use
Pressure cooking
Boiling
Steaming
Waterless
Soup
Pickling
Oilless sautéing (with water)
Pressing

Occasional use
Sautéing*
Stir-frying*
Raw*
Deep-frying*
Tempura*
Baking*

Cooking Aspects to Change for Variety:

1. Selection of foods within the categories of grains, vegetables, beans,
   sea vegetables, and so on;
2. Methods of cooking;
3. Ways of cutting vegetables;
4. Amount of water used;
5. Amount and kind of seasoning and condiments used;

32

6. Length of cooking time;
7. Use of a higher or lower flame;
8. Varying the combination of foods and dishes;
9. Seasonal cooking adjustments.

Way of Life Suggestions and Reminders ────────────

- Maintain the dream and image of health, peace, and abundance for yourself, others and the world.
- Live each day happily without being preoccupied with your health, stay mentally and physically alert and active.
- View everything and everyone you meet with gratitude. Offer thanks before and after each meal.
- It is best to retire before midnight and get up early in the morning, especially with the sunrise.
- It is best to avoid wearing synthetic or woolen clothing directly against the skin. Wear cotton as much as possible, especially for undergarments. Avoid excessive metallic accessories on the fingers, wrists, or neck. Keep such ornaments simple and graceful.
- If your strength permits, go outdoors in simple clothing. Walk on the grass, beach, or soil up to one half hour every day.
- Keep you home (and other surroundings) in good order, from the kitchen, bathroom, bedroom, living room, to every corner of the house.
- Initiate and maintain an active correspondence, extending best wishes to your family and friends. Also maintain and initiate good relationships with everyone around you.
- Avoid taking long hot baths or showers unless you have been consuming too much salt or animal food.
- Scrub your entire body with a hot, damp towel until the skin becomes red, every morning or every night before retiring. If that is not possible, at least scrub your hands, feet, fingers and toes.
- Avoid chemically-perfumed cosmetics. For care of the teeth, brush with natural preparations or sea salt.
- If your condition permits, exercise regularly as part of your daily life, including activities like scrubbing floors, cleaning windows and so on as well as exercise programs such as yoga, dance, sports, and martial arts.
- Avoid using electric cooking devices (ovens or ranges) or microwave ovens. Convert to a gas or wood stove at the earliest opportunity.
- It is best to minimize the frequent use of color television and computer display units.
- Include some large green plants in your house to freshen and enrich the oxygen content of the air in your home.

3. Dietary Adjustments for Diabetes and Hypoglycemia

So far we have looked at the *Standard Macrobiotic Diet*; this is enough to prevent blood glucose problems from developing, and will maintain good health. However, in cases where such problems already exist, it is necessary to make some additional special adjustments in this general dietary plan, to be followed for several months or until the problem is somewhat alleviated (after which the more general standard dietary approach may be adopted).

Both types of disorders reflect a basic extremism or imbalance in the body; so, it is important in either case to avoid overly one-sided eating. Try to present a balanced mix of both yin and yang energies at each meal, and try to cultivate a keen sense of balance in the aesthetic aspects of your cooking, such as how to complement contrasting colors, textures and tastes. Also, it is better to avoid extremes of eating patterns, such as fasting for long periods and then eating a great deal. It may be helpful to eat five or even six smaller meals (as opposed to eating large quantities in one sitting) if three moderate sized meals still leaves you hungry. In general, it is important to avoid overeating (as this can emphasize your body's overreaction or underreaction to carbohydrates).

The most important principle of cooking for these disorders is that foods high in complex carbohydrate—grains and vegetables with an especially sweet taste—are to be emphasized. Here is a list of those vegetables that especially fall into this category: hard squashes (fall or winter varieties, not summer squash or zucchini), pumpkin or Hokkaido pumpkin, onion, green cabbage, rutabaga, turnip, carrot, parsnip, *daikon*, leek, and cauliflower. Among grains, short grain brown rice, sweet brown rice and millet are the most helpful, and among beans and seeds, the smaller varieties (*azuki*, lentils, sesame and pumpkin) are best. The sweetness of fruits and concentrated sweeteners are not usually so helpful to establish balance.

In addition, you will notice that the recommendations for hypoglycemia slightly emphasize more yin energies, while those for diabetes emphasize slightly more yang energies. It bears repeating, though, that all conditions still need both energies, and it is important not to be one-sided.

1. *Whole Cereal Grains:*

A. *For Diabetes:* Emphasize short-grain brown rice, millet and sweet brown rice, occasionally using buckwheat and other grains. Avoid baked flour or processed grains, though occasional use of whole-grain, natural-rise sourdough bread is alright. Boiled flour products such as noodles, *seitan* and *fu* may be eaten on occasion.

B. *For Hypoglycemia:* Emphasize short-grain and medium-grain brown rice, millet, sweet brown rice, barley and pearl barley with other grains for variety. Avoid baked flour products and breads. Noodles, bulgur, cracked wheat or rye, *seitan* and *fu* may be eaten from time to time.

2. *Soups:* Use sweet vegetables regularly.

A. *For Diabetes:* Limit volume to one or two bowls of soup per day. Make sure to have a small amount of sea vegetable (*wakame* or *kombu*) in your soup everyday. For strength, you may use pieces of *mochi* in your *miso* soup from time to time.

B. *For Hypoglycemia:* Be particularly careful that your *miso* or *tamari* soup is not too salty. In addition to sweet vegetables, you may occasionally use *shiitake* mushrooms in soup to help break down animal fat. Barley mushroom soup is helpful for this.

3. *Vegetables:*

In both cases, emphasize sweet vegetables such as buttercup, butternut and Hokkaido squashes as well as carrots, onions and parsnips.

A. *For Diabetes:* Emphasize root vegetables and leafy greens with a complex leaf structure (e.g., kale, watercress, turnip tops) as well as sweet vegetables. Limit the vegetables listed "for occasional use." A dish of sautéed vegetables or fried rice with vegetables may be consumed from time to time. Minimize raw salads, particularly in the winter.

B. *For Hypoglycemia:* Emphasize sweet vegetables with a round shape (e.g., squashes, cabbage, onions, rutabagas) and all leafy vegetables. Sweet vegetables cooked *nishime* style or with *azuki* beans may be eaten often. Use "occasional use" vegetables from time to time. Emphasize quick boiling or blanching, and pressed salads. Raw salads may be eaten occasionally.

4. *Beans and Bean Products:*

In both cases, a small dish of *azuki* beans, hard squash or pumpkin and *kombu*, well-cooked and seasoned with *tamari* soy sauce (more lightly seasoned for hypoglycemia and more richly seasoned for diabetes) may be eaten often or daily. Other sweet vegetables, such as onions, carrots or parsnips, may be used instead of squash if these are not available. Garnish your beans with raw scallions, parsley or finely chopped celery leaves.

A. *For Diabetes:* Preferably limit your use to *azuki* beans and lentils for the first three to six months. Emphasize more dried rather than fresh *tofu*.

B. *For Hypoglycemia:* Emphasize *azuki* beans and lentils using "occasional use" beans and bean products from time to time for variety. Be careful to eat "occasional use" beans in smaller portions as too much fat in a meal can cause the amount of blood glucose to be lowered. Rice vinegar may be used as an occasional seasoning.

5. *Sea Vegetables:* —————————————————————————

A. *For Diabetes:* All types are fine; especially emphasize *kombu*, *arame* and *hijiki*. A side dish of *arame* or *hijiki* cooked with roots or sweet vegetables and seasoned with *tamari* soy sauce and several drops of oil may be eaten 2–3 times per week.

B. *For Hypoglycemia.* All types are fine; especially emphasize *kombu*, *arame*, *wakame* and *nori*. A side dish of *arame* cooked with sweet-tasting vegetables and seasoned lightly with *tamari* soy sauce may be eaten two to three times per week. Several drops of rice vinegar may also be used on occasion if desired.

6. *Seeds, Nuts and Snacks:* ————————————————————

A. *For Diabetes:* Use sesame, black sesame, squash or pumpkin seeds, lightly toasted and salted with sea salt or *tamari* soy sauce. A small volume of lightly roasted peanuts or almonds may also be eaten as a snack, as can rice cakes or unsweetened puffed grains.

B. *For Hypoglycemia:* All roasted and very lightly salted or unsalted seeds are okay as long as not too many are eaten at one time. Lightly roasted and very lightly salted or unsalted peanuts or almonds may be eaten alone or together with dried Northern fruits (currants, berries, apples, etc.) as a frequent snack in moderate volumes.

7. *Seafood:* ————————————————————————————

A. *For Diabetes:* A small amount of white-meat fish may be eaten occasionally, up to twice a week, if strongly desired or needed for strength. Garnish with raw grated *daikon* and *tamari* soy sauce, finely chopped onion or scallion or natural horseradish.

B. *For Hypoglycemia:* It's best to limit fish and seafood for the initial period of a few months. *Seitan* or well-cooked beans seasoned with *miso* may be used to help satisfy the craving for fish or animal foods. If you still crave fish, occasionally have a small amount of soft white-meat fish, avoiding red-meat varieties.

8. *Desserts:*

Satisfy your desire for sweet-tasting food with your sweet grains, vegetable and bean dishes. If desired, a natural dessert may also be eaten several times per week, emphasizing grains, beans, vegetables and grain based sweeteners. More infrequently, a small amount of cooked or dried fruits may be used.

9. *Seasonings:*

A. *For Diabetes:* Sea salt, *miso*, *tamari* soy sauce and *umeboshi* may all be used regularly to achieve a slightly rich taste. However, overuse of these can make you very thirsty and it is important to keep liquid intake to a comfortable minimum, so be careful to use salty seasonings only moderately. You may need to regularly adjust this level to your changing needs. A small amount of sesame or roasted (dark) sesame oil may be used occasionally for frying or sautéing (but avoid using raw oil in dressings). It is very important to get the best quality oil you can. Other macrobiotic seasonings (ginger, rice vinegar, etc.) may be used occasionally.

B. *For Hypoglycemia:* It is best to go light on all salty seasonings. A small strip of *kombu* or any other sea vegetable may sometimes substitute for salt seasoning in some dishes (e.g., *nishime* vegetables). The use of all oils is limited until the hypoglycemic condition begins to improve. Other macrobiotic seasonings may be used occasionally in small reasonable amounts.

10. *Table Condiments and Pickles:*

A. *For Diabetes:* Use *gomashio*, with a proportion of 12–14 parts roasted sesame seeds to 1 part sea salt, daily or regularly. It is best to use only homemade *gomashio*. Baked and ground *kombu* or *wakame* powder, alone or ground with crushed toasted sesame or pumpkin seeds can be used as well as *nori* and green *nori* flakes. More occasionally, use *tekka* and *shio kombu*. Emphasize pickles made from cabbage, kale or other hard leafy greens and *daikon* and other roots which are pickled for a minimum of several days (longer is best) in sea salt brine, rice bran and sea salt, or sea salt alone. Long-term (three months or more) rice bran or *miso* pickles are especially helpful for sound digestion and a stronger overall condition, though they should be consumed in very small amounts at a time.

B. *For Hypoglycemia:*   Daily or regularly, use homemade *gomashio* with a proportion of 14–16 parts roasted sesame seeds to 1 part sea salt. Sea vegetable powders, with or without roasted and crushed seeds, as well as *nori*, green *nori* flakes, *shiso* leaves, *shio nori* and some occasional rice vinegar may also be used. All macrobiotic quality, unspiced pickles may be used. Just be careful that, if salty, only very small amounts are consumed.

11. *Beverages:*

A. *For Diabetes:*   In general, consumption of liquids may be moderate, especially using *bancha* (*kukicha*) twig tea, roasted cereal grain or root "coffees" or teas. It is better to limit juices, mineral waters and other more occasional types of beverages.

B. *For Hypoglycemia:*   The volume of drinking may be somewhat more liberal while avoiding all cold drinks, soft drinks, sugar sweetened drinks and stimulating or highly aromatic beverages including coffee.

4. Understanding Diabetes and Hypoglycemia

As we saw in the previous sections of this book, human life is not an isolated, independent phenomena but the end result of a long, natural spiral of creation. This spiral of creation is not something that happened once, long ago, but is actually happening right now and at every moment.

We are constantly connected with, created, and nourished by our universal origin through the food, water, air, light, thoughts, the polarizing energies of yin and yang (shown in the rhythmic contractions and expansions of our lungs or heart or the complementary secretions of insulin and anti-insulin from our endocrine system and so on) as well as direct streams of infinite consciousness which enables us to have a sense of oneness, God or absolute faith.

Health depends on maintaining an unblocked, effortless flow of energy between these worlds of nourishment in the larger sense. In the smaller but just as powerful dimension of physical, materialized food, health depends on making an effective use of the energy from the carbohydrates which we consume. The essence of vegetable life and of food itself is the carbohydrate which has always been our primary source of food energy, whether the complex carbohydrate (starch or polysaccharide) of whole grains, beans and vegetables, or the simple sugars of white bread, pastries and candy in the modern world. The form of the carbohydrates we eat is one of the most important factors in our health.

If our food is unbalanced, our ability to use the energy of carbohydrate is thrown off. Simply put, if we rely too much on more extreme yang foods, such as eggs, meat, poultry or cheese, we begin to develop hypoglycemia (chronically low or unstable blood glucose); and if we rely too much on more extreme yin foods, including milk, white flour, sugar or honey, soft drinks, and so on, we may begin to develop diabetes. In many cases, we may even develop both tendencies at the same time; and in any of these cases, the central issue is that we lack the stabilizing energy of complex, unrefined carbohydrates. (A thorough explanation of the cause and detailed physiological mechanisms of diabetes and hypoglycemia is presented in the companion to this volume, *Diabetes and Hypoglycemia* [*Macrobiotic Health Education Series*] by Michio Kushi.)

Some modern approaches to these problems can be very ineffective. For example, a diet high in protein and fat is often recommended for hypoglycemia; but this generally means eating a lot of animal food, which is the principle cause of hypoglycemia. This approach is unfortunate as it disregards the balance of yin and yang.

The macrobiotic way to solve these problems is to restore carbohydrate balance and avoid these extreme foods. For diabetic or hypoglycemic persons it is helpful to make some specific adjustments, fine-tuning the standard dietary suggestions to adapt to the particular person and problem, for an initial period of several months. This is best done with the guidance of a qualified counselor or health professional who is experienced with the macrobiotic diet; but the general guidelines given in this book and the companion volume are enough to get you started. Basically, the diet can slightly emphasize more yin energy to help relieve hypoglycemia, and slightly more yang energy to help relieve diabetes. And in both cases, it is helpful to eat some distinctly sweet-tasting grain and vegetable dishes everyday.

How quickly the condition changes depends upon the particular case. But generally, most cases of hypoglycemia and mild (Type 2) diabetes can be relieved substantially in three to six months, with more difficult cases taking somewhat longer.

Though it is what we are basically concerned with in this book, it is always important to remember that adjusting our physical food is not an isolated solution. Remember to stay mentally and physically active and maintain good relationships with the people and the world around us.

5. Menu Planning ━━━━━━━━━━━

When planning a menu, there are several things to consider.

1. The relative proportions of grains, vegetables, soup, beans, and so on in a meal as recommended in the *Standard Macrobiotic Diet*.
2. Adjustments for diabetic and hypoglycemic conditions (see *Dietary Adjustments for Diabetes and Hypoglycemia* chapter).
3. Make sure that there is variety in your meals by varying:
   A. The types of vegetables and grains used. Everyday have some kind of root vegetable, fresh and leafy greens and in some form, a small amount of sea vegetable. It is helpful to have brown rice everyday but there are many ways you can vary this basic dish as you will see in the menu examples.
   B. The seasonings, condiments and pickles used. (It is preferred that one has a small amount of pickles daily.)
   C. The cooking methods employed. Everyday, have some quickly boiled or blanched greens as well as pressure-cooked or longer time cooked items.
   D. The sizes, shapes, colors and textures from dish to dish. Use attractive garnishes to brighten your meals.
4. Seasonal and climatic adjustments. For hot weather, emphasize more fresh, lightly boiled or steamed vegetables, salads, less cooking time and less oil and salt, For colder weather, emphasize more hearty, rich dishes, stews and thick soups, protein such as found in beans, root vegetables and a little more salt and oil.
5. Adjustments for the time of day. Beans, hardy dishes, and stronger seasonings are best eaten for dinner. It is recommended that lunches and breakfasts be kept simple and light otherwise one may feel heavy and sluggish throughout the day. Soft porridges and whole grain cereals are delicious for breakfast.
6. Adjustments for age. For babies, younger children and elderly persons, serve more soft foods and sweet tasting vegetables with a minimum amount of seasonings. It is preferred that babies don't eat any salt at all. Teens and adults can have more seasonings and more crisp, solid vegetables.
7. Life-style adjustments. People doing more physical exercise, work and activities need more protein and hardy, rich dishes than someone who is more sedentary.
8. Use as much of your leftovers as you can. The menus below disregard leftovers to emphasize variety but normally a grain or bean dish, for

42

example, can last for several days or more. Besides simply reheating leftovers you can also rework them into a new format; for instance, last night's dinner rice can be this mornings soft rice. Or you might want to add a few pieces of *tofu* when heating up yesterday's root vegetables. The possibilities are endless. All this adds more appeal and variety to your meals. There is one thing to watch out for and that is that one should *Have Fresh, Quickly Boiled or Blanched Leafy Greens Everyday*. Therefore, boil only as much greens as you can have in one meal.

A General Seven Day Menu for Diabetic and Hypoglycemic Persons ——————

		DIABETICS	HYPOGLYCEMIA
1	B	*Miso* Soft Rice	*Miso* Soft Rice
		Bancha Tea	*Bancha* Tea
	L	*Soba* in Broth w/Scallions	*Udon* in Broth w/Scallions
		Boiled Mustard Greens & Onions	Boiled Mustard Greens & Onions
		Takuan Pickles	Quick-pressed Radish Pickles
		Mugicha Tea	*Mugicha* Tea
	D	*Tofu*/Watercress *Tamari* Soup	*Tofu*/Watercress *Tamari* Soup
		Pressure-cooked Brown Rice	Pressure-cooked Brown Rice
		Azuki Beans/Squash/*Kombu*	*Azuki* Beans/Squash/*Kombu*
		Dried *Daikon* & *Kombu*	Dried *Daikon* & *Kombu*
		Boiled Collard Greens	Boiled Collard Greens
		Onion Pickles	Onion Pickles
		Bancha Tea	*Bancha* Tea
2	B	Barley Porridge w/*Gomashio*	Barley Porridge w/*Gomashio*
		Grain Tea	Grain Tea
	L	Rice Balls	Rice Balls
		Boiled Salad (Chinese Cabbage, Carrots, Watercress, Sesame Seeds)	Boiled Salad (Chinese Cabbage, Carrots, Watercress, Sesame Seeds)
		Quick-pressed Radish Pickles	Quick-pressed *Daikon* Pickles
		Bancha Tea	*Bancha* Tea
	D	*Miso* Soup w/Sautéed Vegetables	*Miso* Soup w/Chinese Cabbage & *Shiitake* Mushrooms
		Sweet Rice with Millet	Sweet Rice with Millet
		Tempeh Onions & Parsnips	*Kombu*/Onions/Burdock/Turnips
		Steamed or Boiled Broccoli	Steamed or Boiled Broccoli
		Shio Kombu	*Nori* Condiment
		Mugicha Tea	*Mugicha* Tea

3	B	*Mochi* w/Grated *Daikon*	*Mochi* w/Grated *Daikon*
		Miso Soup w/Scallions	*Miso* Soup w/Scallions
		Bancha Tea	*Bancha* Tea
	L	Millet & Squash	Millet & Squash
		Boiled Kale	*Wakame* Salad
		Broccoli Stem *Miso* Pickles	Broccoli Stem *Miso* Pickles
		Mugicha Tea	*Migicha* Tea
	D	Fish Soup	*Tamari* Broth w/Onion & Carrots
		Azuki Bean Rice	Rice with Barley
		Onion/Cabbage/Squash/*Kombu*	Boiled *Daikon* & Its Greens
		Wakame & Ginger	*Tempeh*/Onions/Parsnips
		Boiled Mustard Greens	Boiled Mustard Greens
		Quick-pressed Chinese Cabbage Pickles	*Shio Kombu*
		Applesauce	*Aamzake* Pudding
		Bancha Tea	*Bancha* Tea

4	B	Millet Porridge	Millet Porridge
		Shiso Leaf Condiment	*Shiso* Leaf Condiment
		Mugicha Tea	*Mugicha* Tea
	L	Fried Rice w/Vegetables	*Arepas*
		Boiled Cauliflower	Boiled Kale
		Onion/Cucumber Brine Pickles	Onion/Cucumber Brine Pickles
		Grain Tea	Grain Tea
	D	*Miso* Soup w/*Daikon* & *Wakame*	*Miso* Soup w/*Daikon* & *Wakame*
		Rice with Barley	Boiled Brown Rice
		Seitan Stew w/Onion/Rutubagas/ Brussels Sprouts	Carrots/Cauliflower/Onions
		Boiled Watercress & Chinese Cabbage	Boiled Watercress
		Tofu Pickles	Chinese Cabbage/*Nori*/Flat *Fu*
		Bancha Tea	*Tofu* Pickles
			Bancha Tea

5	B	Plain Soft Rice w/*Nori* & *Umeboshi*	Soft Rice w/*Nori* & *Umeboshi*
		Mugicha Tea	*Mugicha* Tea
	L	*Sushi*	*Sushi*
		Boiled Collard Greens	Boiled Collard Greens
		Takuan Pickles	Quick-pressed Chinese Cabbage Pickles
		Mu Tea	*Mu* Tea
	D	Lentil Soup	Barley/*Shiitake* Soup
		Sesame Seed Rice	Sesame Seed Rice
		Pressure-cooked Buttercup or Hokkaido Squash	Pressure-cooked Buttercup or Hokkaido Squash
		Arame/Dried *Tofu*/Onions/Parsnips	*Arame*/Dried *Tofu*/Onions/ Parsnips
		Boiled Kale	

44

		Califlower/Radish Brine Pickles	Boiled Kale
		Grain Coffee	Califlower/Radish Brine Pickles
			Grain Coffee

6 B *Miso* Soft Rice   *Miso* Soft Rice
     Bancha Tea   *Bancha* Tea
  L *Zaru Soba*   Millet/Carrots/Onions
     Boiled Chinese Cabbage/   Boiled Chinese Cabbage/
       Watercress/Sesame Seeds   Watercress/Sesame Seeds
     Onion Pickles   Onion Pickles
     Mugicha Tea   *Mugicha* Tea
  D *Tamari* Broth Soup   *Tamari* Broth Soup
     Pressure-cooked Brown Rice   Pressure-cooked Brown Rice
     Black Soybeans   Black Soybeans
     Carrot/Burdock *Kinpira* w/Oil   Carrot/Burdock/*Kinpira* without Oil
     Boiled Broccoli & Cauliflower   Boiled Broccoli & Cauliflower
     Lotus Root/*Wakame*/*Shiitake*   Lotus Root/*Wakame*/*Shiitake*
       Brine Pickles   Brine Pickles
     Bancha Tea   *Bancha* Tea

7 B Creamy *Kasha* w/*Gomashio*   Barley Porridge w/*Wakame* Powder
     Mugicha Tea   *Mugicha* Tea
  L *Arepas*   Boiled Couscous
     Miso Soup w/*Daikon* & *Wakame*   *Miso* Soup w/*Daikon* & *Wakame*
     Boiled Mustard Greens   Boiled Mustard Greens
     Bancha Tea   *Bancha* Tea
  D Millet Squash Soup   Millet Squash Soup
     Azuki Bean Rice   *Azuki* Bean Rice
     Tempeh & Vegetables   Dried *Tofu* w/*Daikon* Stew
     Boiled Collard Greens   Boiled Collard Greens
     Amazake Pudding   Applesauce
     Chinese Cabbage Bran Pickles   Chinese Cabbage Bran Pickles
     Grain Tea   Grain Tea

Snacks: Rice Cakes (can use onion butter on them), Dry Roasted Peanuts, Leftovers, *Mochi*, Unbuttered Popcorn, Unsweetened Puffed Cereals, Roasted Pumpkin or Sesame Seeds with or without Raisins.

6. Cookware ▰▰▰▰▰▰▰▰▰▰▰

Along with stocking the kitchen with good food, you need to equip it with a collection of essential cookware. Having the right tools in front of you makes all the difference in your cooking experience by freeing your mind to work with a more relaxed and creative attitude. This naturally has a profound effect on your well-being as well as affecting the quality, taste and appeal of your meals. Also, some types of kitchen equipment should best be avoided as they are suspected to be detrimental to your health, while others are a must for their beneficial influences. Listed below is a checklist of what you'll need.

1. We recommend a gas stove as opposed to an electric one. There are several reasons for this:

   A. Electricity dissipates the molecular structure and strength of your food by causing the electrons to bounce out of the atomic field and leaving the atom very unstable. Gas, on the other hand, just bounces the molecules around, while leaving them intact.

   B. It's very hard to fine tune your cooking with electricity. It is a conductive heat which first warms the coils and then the pot and its contents from the bottom up. You can't change the temperature quickly when turning to high or low because it takes some time to cool or heat the pot. It's difficult to cook uniformly and it's possible that the bottom can burn while the top needs more cooking. A gas flame heats the air around it instead. The food is cooked much more evenly and the temperature can be adjusted immediately (a pot of water will instantly stop boiling the moment you turn off the flame, for example). Meals are more well cooked.

   C. Because of these drawbacks in electric cooking, a person may not feel satisfied with the meal and may crave strong salt or animal food (to counter the yin and weakening effects) which in turn causes a craving for excessive sweets and other yin foods. In other words, it becomes more of a struggle to eat in a balanced manner and stay on the macrobiotic diet.

   A microwave oven is definitely out of the picture and should be avoided, particularly if you are sick. It zaps your food with radio-active waves at three billion cycles per second (a regular electric stove runs at 60 cycles per second and is actually a low form of radiation). It disintegrates instead of cooks and can cause the same effect in your body. Not only does it not help you to regain your health but it is suspected by some people to contribute to illnesses. Recent studies have shown that it produces tumors in mice.

After gas, wood is the best source of heat (followed by coal or charcoal) though it is impractical for most modern homes. It has a peaceful energy and at the same time it gives great strength.

2. Several stainless steel pots of varying sizes. The steel doesn't interfere with the energies of the food. It's best to avoid aluminum because it is a poisonous substance and under high temperatures or when cooking very acidic (sweet) or alkaline (salty) foods, harmful toxins are released and mixed in with your ingredients.

    Cookware made out of glass (like pyrex), earthenware, and enamelware are also excellent materials to cook in. (Be careful that you don't pour cold water into a heated enamel pot or leave it empty over a flame as this will cause it to crack. Let it cool off before you attempt to wash it. It is also easily scratched so don't clean it with a steel wool scrubber and use a wooden spoon when handling food inside it.)

3. At least one pressure-cooker (stainless or enamel steel). This is an ideal pot for cooking grains, beans, root vegetables (like big chunks of burdock), squash, or anything that takes a long-time to soften. The nutrients are better retained and everything is cooked more thoroughly, quickly and with more energy than when prepared in a regular pot.

    To use, put ingredients inside (not more than ¾ full), cover (don't forget to put the weight attachment on top) and over a medium high flame, bring it up to pressure. You can tell it's up when there is a lot of hissing and the weight begins to jiggle and shake. Then, immediately turn down the flame and, if needed, place a heat deflector underneath. Simmer (anywhere from 5–10 minutes to an hour or more depending on what's inside) until the food is done. Take the pot off the stove and let the pressure come down. You can let it come down naturally or rinse the pot under cold running water in the sink. This brings it down right away.

    I should add that before you cook, carefully take a good look at the cover. Inspect the hole (on which you place the weight) and make sure that it isn't clogged. Otherwise, an explosion can occur when the pressure is high. Also, look at the rubber rings on the inside of the lid and in the pot itself where the rings touch. Remove any bits of food or other substances which may be stuck there as they will create a gap where steam can escape and as a result, the pressure will never build up.

4. Several cast-iron skillets for roasting and sautéing. Season them when you first get them and from time to time thereafter. To do this, wash and dry them thoroughly. Rub sesame oil all over (outside also) with a paper towel. You can coat the inside by rotating and tilting the pan over a flame. Place them in the oven at 225°–250° F. for 2–3 hours. Then, let them sit for a few hours until they cool. Seasoning prevents the pans from rusting. For the same reason, don't soak them in hot, soapy water, and dry them thoroughly over a low flame after you wash them.

5. One deep cast-iron pot for deep-frying. Cast-iron is the best material to hold the intense heat of the oil.

6. Baking containers including pie plates, bread pans, muffin tins, and so on. Again, avoid aluminum.

7. An optional *wok* (a Chinese-style skillet). The cast-iron skillets can effectively cover your sautéing needs but a *wok* is great for quick, light and fast cooking vegetables and fish.

8. Several stainless steel mixing bowls in different sizes for washing and mixing your food.

9. Large wooden serving bowls for your grains. Wood gives your grains room to breathe as well as retarding their spoilage as they absorb any excess water. You need to oil the bowls periodically to prevent them from cracking. Heat some sesame oil, pour it into a completely dry bowl which you rotate until the inside is completely oiled. Oil the outside also, with a brush or paper towel. Let it sit for a few hours until it dries completely.

Fig. 5 *Suribachi* and pestle

10. Various other attractive serving containers made of glass, china, or ceramics. (Plastic is to be avoided.)

11. A stainless steel or bamboo steamer.

12. A colander for rinsing noodles and other foods.

13. A fine strainer for washing seeds and grains.

14. A *suribachi* and pestle for making *gomashio* and other condiments. This is a Japanese ceramic bowl with grooves, made for crushing roasted sesame seeds, sea vegetables and so on.

15. A food mill for puréeing cooked grains and vegetables. (An electric blender is more disruptive to the energies of foods. Instead of using one on a regular basis I like to save it for parties or special occasions when working with large volumes.)

16. A grain mill for grinding grains and nuts into flour. Flour is best when used soon after grinding. It immediately starts to oxidize and begins to lose some of its nutrients. Also, it is most delicious when fresh. (Your local natural food store may have a good supply of flour as well.)

17. A pickle press for making pickles and pressed salads.

18. An earthenware crock with a wide mouth is good for making bran pickles among other things.

19. Tea pot or kettle. Avoid aluminum.

20. A tea strainer for straining out leaves and twigs when serving the tea. A bamboo one, found in natural food and Oriental stores is the best one to use.

Fig. 6   Tea strainer

21. Large glass jars for storing grains, beans, nuts, seeds and other foods as well as for making pickles.

22. Wooden cutting boards. Keep a separate one for fish and animal foods as their bacteria can have a toxic effect on vegetables.

23. Knives. The square shaped Oriental knives are the easiest and the most efficient. They come in;
    A. carbon (which has a good sharp edge but rusts and chips easily),
    B. stainless steel (which doesn't rust but isn't as sharp), and
    C. high-grade carbon with stainless steel which doesn't rust and is sharp as well (but is more expensive).

Fig. 7   Vegetable knife

To protect the carbon knives, wash them in warm, soapy water and dry them immediately, right after you use them. If rust starts to appear, scrape it off with a steel wool scrubber. Along with keeping your knives as dry as possible, they may be coated with a little sesame oil after use.

You will want to get a sharpening stone along with a knife to keep the edges of your knives sharp. Oil the stone with a vegetable oil or rinse it in water before you use it. Tilt the knife at a 20 degree angle and sweep the blade against the stone in several circular motions. You can use one of your hands to press down upon the blade while the other hand holds the knife and moves it in circles. Sharpen the entire length of the edge. You may choose to sharpen just one side for more control (the right side for right handers and the left side for lefties). Do not use this knife for bread as its blade may be destroyed.

24. A bread knife. The best knife for cutting bread has a long, thin blade with a serrated edge.

25. A grater, most often used for grating fresh ginger, *daikon*, carrots, onions, lotus root, *jinenjo*, and taro potato in macrobiotic cooking.

Fig. 8   Grater

26. A vegetable peeler, good for removing skins of cucumbers, apples and so on, when necessary.

27. A flame or heat deflector. This thin metal plate is placed under the pot or pressure-cooker to even the flame and to help prevent the food from burning. Don't use the white asbestos deflector as asbestos is poisonous.

28. An oil skimmer for lifting small bits of batter and food from *tempura* oil as well as for lifting vegetables from a pot of water.

29. A natural bristle brush for brushing oil into a skillet, cookie sheets, muffin tins, pie plates and so on. Any small, clean, unused brush can be used.

30. Drop tops. These tops fit inside the pot and sit directly on top of the food you are cooking, especially effective in cooking beans. They add some pressure but let steam escape and thus the food is cooked more thoroughly and softens more quickly.

31. Drop tops for pickles made in a keg such as bran pickles. A wooden one is the best. A heavy stone or weight is placed on top for pressure. A plate is a good substitute if a wooden one can't be found.

32. A vegetable brush with natural bristles is best for washing vegetables. They can be found in natural or Oriental food stores.

33. Wooden spoons for stirring, mixing, scooping and serving food before and after you cook. Wood has the best energy in interaction with your food as well as being more gentle to your pots, pans and bowls. Wooden spoons don't scratch cookware.

34. A bamboo rice paddle for handling and serving your grains.

Fig. 9 Rice paddle

35. Soup ladles.

36. Rubber spatula for scraping batter, puréed food and so on from bowls and pots.

37. A metal spatula for turning food over.

38. Cooking chopsticks. These are longer than the table version.

39. A rolling pin.

40. Measuring cups and spoons.

41. Sushi mats for making *sushi* and covering cooked food. (They let air circulate and help retard spoilage).

42. Bamboo mats. Also for covering food.

43. 100 percent cotton cheesecloths, used as covers when making pickles and also for making little sacks to contain foods in cooking (sort of like a tea bag).

44. Paper towels.

7. Cooking Attitude ▬▬▬▬▬▬▬

Besides the food and cookware, to be a good cook you need to have the right attitude and frame of mind. Here is another check list.

1. Leave all your worries, problems, and angers behind as you relax your mind and body into a peaceful, calm state of being. All your thoughts and emotions get mixed into the food and have an effect on anyone who eats it. Here are some things, among others, which you can think about as you cook:

   A. Pour your love and healing vibrations into your food and imagine that whoever eats it will become healthier and happier.
   B. Imagine that the food has the power to help realize everyone's dreams and that with this tool you have the ability to vitalize and inspire whole civilizations, because you do.
   C. In your mind, thank the farmer, trucker, store keeper, mother nature, the food itself, cookware companies and anyone else who has made it possible for you to have these wonderful ingredients and utensils in front of you.
   D. Imagine that you are composing a symphony or painting a masterpiece as you combine colors, textures, tastes and smells into beautiful and dynamic combinations. Release your creativity and intuition more and more, day by day.
   E. Realize that there is always more to learn. Don't ever become arrogant and think that you know it all. Be open and you can learn from everyone around you. We all have different perspectives and ideas and therefore we all have something to offer.

2. Clean and organize your kitchen and surroundings before, during and after you cook.

3. If you have long hair, tie it back to help prevent it from catching on fire as well as from falling into the food. Wear a clean apron and roll up your sleeves.

4. Work quickly, calmly and efficiently, economically making the most of your time. Avoid munching while you cook as this will really slow you down.

5. Keep other activities and distractions to a minimum and concentrate all your energies in your cooking.

6. When making your menu, first look at all your leftovers and older vegetables and use these first. Don't waste any food. Don't buy more perishables than you need. Look first at your supply before you go shopping.

7. Develop your intuition and common sense so that you can appropriately adapt your meals to the weather, the season, the people for whom you are cooking with their daily needs and changes, your own moods and any other influencing factors for that particular place and time.

8. Keep your meals simple. Don't mash together dozens of different ingredients into one dish. Go light on your seasonings and use them mainly to draw out and enhance the natural flavors of your food.

9. Decorate your food beautifully, set the table using appealing tableware, and make your dining area comfortable and aesthetically pleasing. This enhances your appetite and dining experience.

10. Take the time and place to relax, sit down and peacefully enjoy your meal with appreciation. Chew your food thoroughly, the saliva helps digestion. Also, it is best not to eat unless one is truly hungry.

8. Grains and Grain Products

The most helpful dishes for regular use include:

For Both Disorders:

> **Short-grain brown rice, pressure-cooked**
> **Millet; rice and millet, millet and sweet vegetables**
> **Sweet rice with millet**
> ***Azuki* rice**

For Diabetes:

> **Rice balls**
> **Fried rice with vegetables**
> ***Seitan* stew, *seitan* with vegetables**
> ***Soba* in broth**

For Hypoglycemia:

> **Soft rice**
> **Soft millet**
> **Brown rice with barley**
> **Boiled brown rice**

Grains stored in a cool, dark, dry location can be kept forever. (Get them organic as much as possible.) To retain the maximum energy of your grains, leave grains unhusked until you cook with them if possible.

Before you wash grains, spread a handful at a time onto a plate and remove any stones and other debris which may be mixed in. Then, place the grains in a bowl (the lightweight stainless steel mixing bowls are excellent for this), cover with cold water and very gently stir and rinse off any dirt that floats to the top until the water becomes clear. Then, place the grain in a colander or strainer. (Wash quickly to help retain as many nutrients in the grain as possible.)

There are several kinds of grains that are available:

Brown Rice:

Brown rice, being the easiest to digest, is the most suitable grain for daily use. You can have it everyday, regardless of whether you are in the transitional, healing or standard phase. We eat it at almost every meal. The other grains serve as variations, either as a substitute or as an additional ingredient in a meal. We mainly use four types of rice:

1. *Short-grain:*   It is the variety with the hardiest taste and energy and the most effective one for creating a healthy balanced condition in your body. Use this one most of the time, especially in the winter.
2. *Medium-grain:*   This is more soft and moist and is a nice variation.
3. *Long-grain:*   This is light and fluffy, excellent for fried rice, and makes a great alternative in the summer and warmer climates.
4. *Sweet rice:*   This is even more sweet and glutinous than the short grain and is quite sticky. This grain can be added to other grains periodically for a sweeter taste, and also serves as a base for *ohagi*, *mochi* and *amazake*.

We recommend pressure-cooking your rice most of the time. This form of preparation cooks the grains more thoroughly, they become easier to digest, are less soggy, more sweet and more healing. Along with the help of a pressure-cooker there are two ways to make your grain softer, sweeter and more digestible;

1. *Non-soaking:*   Start cooking the grain very slowly over a low flame, in an uncovered pressure-cooker. Don't put any salt in yet so that it will take more time to come to a boil. When it comes to a boil, add the salt, cover and bring it up to pressure (it is up when the gauge hisses). Then, place a heat deflector underneath (make sure the flame is on medium low) and simmer for 45–50 minutes.
2. *Soaking:*   Soak the rice (covered with cold water) for 3–5 hours or overnight. Place in the pressure-cooker (along with the soaking water). This time, add salt and cover right away (otherwise it may turn out too soggy). Put on a medium high flame and bring it up to pressure. When it is up, turn the flame down to medium low, place a heat deflector underneath and simmer for 45–50 minutes.

Basic Brown Rice (Pressure-Cooked)
(Use everyday, the principle food for all conditions.)

> 3 cups organic brown rice
> 3 ¾–4 ½ cups spring water
> 3 pinches sea salt

Pressure-cook following one of the above methods. Let the pressure come down completely before removing the cover. Scoop out the rice with a wet rice paddle or wooden spoon into a wooden bowl as you separate and air out the lumps.

The bottom rice can be mixed in if it's not burnt. Keep the brown side turned down and totally covered to help keep it soft. If the bottom is really stuck to the pot, keep a 1″ layer of rice in the pot, put the lid back on, and let it sit for 20–30 minutes. The warmth of the fresh rice will help to loosen and soften the bottom.

Keep the rice covered with a bamboo or *sushi* mat. They protect it while letting it have air to breathe. Then dish the rice into individual bowls and serve. Serves 6.

There are many variations that you can use. Below are four helpful recipes followed by a partial listing of other variations.

Azuki Bean Rice
(Helps strengthen the kidneys and adrenals.)

> 2½ cups brown rice
> ½ cup *azuki* beans
> 4½ cups spring water
> 3 pinches sea salt
> 1 piece *kombu*, 3″–6″ long

Wash *azuki* beans and boil them with the *kombu* in 2 cups of water for 10–15 minutes until the water becomes red. Cool the beans till they are lukewarm. Wash the rice, put it in the pressure-cooker with the beans and the red, boiled juice. Use pressure-cooking method #1 (*Non-soaking*) and follow the directions for *Basic Brown Rice*. Or you can soak the rice and beans together overnight and use method #2 (*Soaking*). Serves 6.

Lotus Seed Rice
(The addition of lotus seeds makes this dish especially strengthening for the lungs and the kidneys.)

> 2½ cups brown rice
> ½ cup lotus seeds
> 4½ cups spring water
> 3 pinches sea salt

Wash and soak lotus seeds and rice 3–4 hours or overnight. Pressure-cook using method #2 and following the directions for *Basic Brown Rice* (*Pressure-cooked*). Serves 6.

Sesame Seed Rice
(Helps improve general vitality.)

> 2½ cups brown rice
> ½ cup roasted white or black sesame seeds
> 3¾–4½ cups spring water
> 3 pinches sea salt

Wash and quickly roast white or black sesame seeds (being careful not to burn them) in a skillet stirring with a wooden spoon until a nutty fragrance is emitted. Combine with all the other ingredients and cook as in *Basic Brown Rice* (*Pressure-cooked*). Serves 6.

Sweet Rice and Millet
(Strengthens spleen, pancreas and stomach.)

2 cups sweet rice
1 cup millet
4 cups spring water
3 pinches sea salt

Wash and combine all the ingredients and cook as in *Basic Brown Rice* (*Pressure-cooked*), method #2 (minus the *soaking*) for 40–45 minutes. Serves 6.

Other variations include:

1) $2\frac{1}{2}$ cups rice + $\frac{1}{2}$ cup barley ($4\frac{1}{2}$ cups water)
2) 2 cups rice + 1 cup millet ($4\frac{1}{2}$ cups water)
3) 2 cups rice + 1 cup sweet rice
4) $2\frac{1}{2}$ cups rice + $\frac{1}{2}$ cup wheat berries (soaked overnight)
5) $2\frac{1}{2}$ cups rice + $\frac{1}{2}$ cup roasted sunflower seeds*
6) $2\frac{1}{2}$ cups rice + $\frac{1}{2}$ cup chickpeas (soaked overnight)
7) 2 cups rice + 1 cup dried chestnuts
8) 2 cups rice + 1 cup fresh corn kernels (3 cups water)
9) $2\frac{1}{2}$ cups rice + $\frac{1}{2}$ cup wild rice
10) $2\frac{1}{2}$ cups rice + $\frac{1}{2}$ cup roasted walnuts*
11) 2 cups rice + 1 *umeboshi* plum (instead of salt)
12) *Bancha* tea instead of water
13) $2\frac{1}{2}$ cups rice + 1 cup squash
14) $2\frac{1}{2}$ cups rice + $\frac{1}{2}$ cup roasted black or yellow soybeans

You can also boil the rice once in a while, particularly for hypoglycemia. It doesn't give you the strength of pressure-cooking but it is a great alternative when you want something lighter, more yin and to add some variety. When you boil your rice, make sure to chew well. You can dry-roast the rice before boiling it for variation.

Basic Brown Rice (Boiled)

2 cups organic brown rice, washed
4 cups spring water
2 pinches sea salt

Put washed rice into a pot (preferably with a heavy lid) with water and salt. Bring to a boil, then lower the flame, place a heat deflector underneath and simmer for about 1 hour or until all the water has been absorbed. Wet a wooden spoon or rice paddle (so the rice won't stick to it) and dish out the rice into a wooden bowl. Keep covered with a *sushi* or bamboo mat. (*Option:* You can roast the rice in a skillet till golden brown before boiling it. This gives more flavor. Gently stir the grains in the skillet with a wooden spoon to prevent them from burning.) Serves 4.

When someone isn't feeling well, we often make soft rice. It is more soothing and is easier on the digestve system. A bowl of it is usually accompanied by an *umeboshi* plum which also helps digestion. Even if you are feeling well, this makes a delicious porridge. If you leave out the salt, this also makes a perfect food for babies and young children.

Soft Rice (Plain)
(A good healing dish.)

> 1 cup brown rice
> 5 cups water
> 1 pinch sea salt

Cook as in *Basic Brown Rice* (*Pressure-cooked*). You can also boil it by simmering it overnight over a low flame and a heat deflector. If you do so, use 10 cups of water to every cup of rice. Serves 5.

People suffering from weak digestion could use a bowl of *miso* soup or a bowl of soft *miso* rice regularly. Below is a soft rice recipe made from cooked brown rice.

Ojiya (Soft Rice with *Miso*)
(Have often while healing.)

> 2 cups leftover cooked brown rice
> 4–5 cups spring water
> 3 Tbsps. (or to taste) *miso* instead of salt
> 1 strip *kombu* (about 4″–6″ long)
> 3–4 sliced scallions

Wash, soak and slice the *kombu* and place it into the bottom of a pot or pressure-cooker. Add the rice and water and bring them up to a boil or to pressure. Turn the flame to low, place a deflector underneath and simmer or pressure-cook for ½ hour. Add 1 tablespoon or so of water to the *miso* and stir it in until the *miso* becomes a purée. Uncover the rice (wait until the pressure is gone if using a pressure-cooker) and then put it back onto the stove. Mix the *miso*, simmer for another 3–5 minutes and turn off the flame. Garnish with sliced scallions and serve immediately. Serves 4–5.

Rice Cream with *Nori* and *Umeboshi*

(Rice cream is a dish with special healing qualities. It helps purify blood and lymph.)

    1 cup dry-roasted brown rice
    3–6 cups spring water
    1 pinch sea salt
    1 toasted sheet of *nori*
    1 *umeboshi* plum
    Cheesecloth

Pressure-cook with sea salt and water for 1 hour following directions for *Basic Brown Rice* (*Pressure-cooked*). Make a sack out of clean cheesecloth. Cool off the cooked rice, place some inside the sack and squeeze out as much of the liquid cream as you can. Reheat and eat this with *nori* and an *umeboshi* plum. The leftover pulp can be eaten separately or added to soup or vegetable dishes. (Occasionally, instead of soaking the rice in the beginning you can dry-roast it in a skillet until golden brown.) Serves 2.

Musubi (Rice Ball)

(Great for lunches, picnics and trips, it is also a very strengthening, stabilizing way to eat rice.)

    1 cup cooked short-grain (sticks well) brown rice
    2 quarters of a *nori* sheet (a sheet cut in half and then half again)
    1 pinch sea salt
    1 *umeboshi* plum (or ½ if it's large)

Toast *nori* by passing it over an open flame a few times till it becomes green but not so much that it becomes crisp and crinkly. Tear it into 4 pieces.

Wet hands (to prevent the rice from sticking to them) in a bowl of salted water, put the rice in your palms and stick an *umeboshi* plum in the middle (the pit may be removed if desired). Tightly mold the rice around the plum into an English muffin shape or a flat triangle and put it down onto a plate.

Wash and dry hands. Then use a quarter of a sheet of *nori* on each side of the rice ball and cover with the shiny side (of the *nori*) on the outside. Firmly mold it on. You can then eat the rice ball or pack it up and take it on a trip to consume later. Serves 1.

Frying is a delicious way to use up your leftover rice. While this method may be used regularly by diabetics, it is better avoided in the case of hypoglycemia.

Fried Rice

3 cups cooked brown rice
1 onion diced
1 sheet of toasted *nori*
5 sliced scallions
1 Tbsp. dark sesame oil
***Tamari* soy sauce to taste**
1 tsp. grated ginger

Heat the oil in a skillet and add diced onions (drop one piece in first and if it sizzles, the oil is hot enough). Stir them a bit with a wooden spoon and then add the rice. Thoroughly mix and stir, breaking up all the big lumps of rice. You can cover, turn the flame to low and let it heat up for about 10 minutes. Then, add soy sauce to taste and simmer for another 3–5 minutes or so. Break up the toasted *nori* into little pieces and mix into the rice along with the scallions and ginger at the end. Serves 2–3.

Mochi is a traditional Japanese dish which is eaten on festive occasions. *Mochi* cakes or squares are made out of pounded sweet rice. Several pieces in *miso* soup can help strengthen the intestines.

Mochi (Homemade)

4 cups sweet rice
4 cups water
4 pinches sea salt
A handful of any finely ground flour (pastry, sweet rice, arrowroot, etc.)

Cook as in *Basic Brown Rice* (*Pressure-cooked*). When done, in a wooden bowl, vigorously pound the rice with a large wooden pestle (which you wet initially and from time to time to prevent the rice from sticking to it) until all the grains are crushed and form a smooth, sticky mass. This may take a half hour. Sprinkle some flour onto a baking sheet and layer the rice on top (up to 1″ thick). Dry this for 1–2 days and then store it in the refrigerator.

When you want to have some, cut the *mochi* into small pieces and toast them in a skillet with or without oil until they become soft. This only takes a few minutes. (Turn them over when they are half done so that both sides toast evenly.) Serve them with some raw grated *daikon* with a few drops of *tamari* soy sauce added. The *daikon* helps in digestion of the *mochi*. Serves 5–6.

Fortunately, you can get previously pounded brown rice *mochi* in some natural food stores. All you have to do is to toast them for a few minutes.

Millet: ————————————————————————

Millet is a more yang grain, being small, round, and more alkaline. It is good for the spleen and pancreas, it helps to settle an acidic stomach and it gives you warmth. For helping to relieve blood glucose disorders, it can be considered as a major grain after rice.

It cooks fairly quickly and comes out very soft so you can, but don't need to pressure-cook it. It can be made either light and fluffy or moist and creamy like a porridge. The fluffy style can be a little too dry, so it can often be eaten with a sauce or cooked with other ingredients. A standard combination uses squash (delicious). Other common companions are vegetables like carrots and onions as well as roasted seeds.

Millet (Dry)

    1 cup millet
    2 cups water
    1 pinch sea salt

Wash the millet. As an option, you may roast it with or without 1 tablespoon of oil in a skillet until a delicious nutty aroma is emitted. (Since allergic persons have to watch their oil content, dry-roast until your condition improves a bit. Stir quickly with a wooden spoon to prevent burning.) Bring the salt and water to a boil and slowly and carefully add the millet. Let this come up to a boil again. Then, cover the pot, turn the flame to medium low, place a heat deflector underneath and simmer for about 30 minutes. Serves 2.

Millet Porridge

    1 cup millet
    4 cups boiling water
    2 pinches sea salt

Bring salt and water to a boil. Wash the millet and carefully pour it into the pot of boiling water. Bring to a boil again, turn the flame to low, place a heat deflector underneath, cover and simmer for 30 minutes. Serves 3.

Millet and Squash

    1 cup millet
    ½ cup buttercup or Hokkaido squash
    2½ cups water
    3 pinches sea salt

Wash and cut the squash into cubes. Remove the seeds and trim away the brown crusted substances on the surface of the skin, if there are any. If the skin happens to be extremely hard, you can slice it off (more a possible problem with the Hokkaido). Place the squash in a pot, put the millet on top, add water and salt, cover and bring to a boil. Then turn the flame to low, place a heat deflector underneath and simmer for 30 minutes. Serves 2–3.

Other variations:

1) **Millet + cauliflower (3 ½ cups water)**
2) **Millet + squash + onions pressure-cooked 15 minutes.**

Barley:

Barley is usually used in combination with other grains (such as rice) and vegetables. It is very mild tasting and lends itself easily to this. Cook it just like rice. It is light and has a cooling, calming energy, particularly helpful for hypoglycemia.

Barley Porridge

1 cup barley
4–5 cups spring water
1 pinch sea salt
Several parsley sprigs

Boil as in *Basic Brown Rice* (*Boiled*). Simmer for 1¼–1½ hours or until soft. Garnish with the parsley. Serves 5.

Buckwheat can grow in a very cold climate and has a short growing season. This grain gives strength, generates heat, and is good for the lungs, kidneys and bladder. It's a great winter food. However, people with hypoglycemia should use this grain only occasionally until their condition clears up.

Buckwheat can be cooked just like millet as it also cooks quickly and is a very soft grain. Below is a recipe for creamy *kasha* (buckwheat).

Creamy *Kasha*

1 cup buckwheat groats
2 scallions
5 cups spring water
1 pinch sea salt

Wash the buckwheat and put it into a pot. Add cold water and sea salt and bring to a boil. Then turn the flame down to low, place a flame deflector underneath and cook for 20–30 minutes. Wash and slice the scallions for a garnish. Serves 3.

Oats: ————————————————————————————

Oats have more protein and fat than other grains. Therefore, while they are helpful to produce more warmth in the body, they shouldn't be taken on a daily basis as they can cause a buildup of mucus. Use about two times a week maximum during the initial healing stage.

You can buy whole oats, cut in half (called Scotch oats) or rolled (what we use for oatmeal). Rolled oats are the most mucus forming, so it is best to use them more occasionally.

Whole Oats

   1 cup whole oats
   5 cups spring water
   1 pinch sea salt
   1 strip *kombu* 3″–6″

Wash and soak oats for 3 hours. Add *kombu* (it helps to cut the fat in the oats) and pressure-cook 2 hours, or boil just like brown rice. If boiling, slowly simmer over a low flame for 3 or more hours or overnight. Serves 3.

Scotch Oats

   1 cup Scotch oats
   3 cups spring water
   1 pinch sea salt
   1 strip *kombu* 3″–6″

Combine water, salt and *kombu* and bring to a boil. Wash and dry-roast the oats in a skillet for 5 minutes, stirring with a wooden spoon over a medium low flame. Then, carefully pour them into the boiling water, bring up to a boil again, turn flame to medium low, place a heat deflector underneath, and cook for about 30–45 minutes. Serves 2.

Oatmeal (Rolled Oats)

Cook as in *Scotch Oats* but for a shorter time. Roast only 2–3 minutes (otherwise they will burn) and simmer for 20–30 minutes.

Wheat: ————————————————————————————

Wheat berries are harder to digest than other grains. They should always be soaked beforehand. Make sure you chew really well in order to insure good digestion.

Pressure-cook like rice except that you need to soak the berries for several hours or overnight. You also may need to cook them an extra

10–15 minutes. Use twice as much water as grain.

You can also get wheat in the form of bulghur, which has been partially boiled, dried and ground, or couscous, which has been refined and cracked. These forms enable you to cook wheat very quickly, especially couscous. These should not be staple foods as a lot of nutrients have been removed in the process. Use them as an occasional treat and variation.

Azuki Bean Wheat Berries

> 2 cups wheat berries
> ½–¾ cup *azuki* beans
> 4–5 cups spring water
> 2 pinches sea salt

Wash and soak berries and beans together for 3–5 hours or overnight. Pressure-cook as in *Basic Brown Rice*. Simmer for 60–70 minutes. Serves 6–8.

Bulghur and Vegetables

> 1 cup bulghur
> ¼ cup each of diced onions, carrots and celery
> 2–2½ cups spring water
> 1 pinch sea salt

Bring salt and water to a boil. Meanwhile, wash and dice the vegetables and layer them (onions on the bottom, then celery and finally carrots on top) into another pot. Add some water (just enough to cover the vegetables) and simmer until they are soft. Then, add the bulghur, pour the boiling water on top, cover and bring to a boil again. Turn the flame to low and simmer for 20 minutes. Serves 3.

Boiled Couscous

> 1 cup couscous
> 2½ cups spring water
> 1 pinch sea salt
> *Optional:* 1 tsp. sesame oil

Bring the water, salt and optional oil to a boil. Pour in the couscous, turn the flame to low, cover and simmer for 5 minutes. Add some garnish or sauce. Serves 2.

Corn:

The corn eaten by the native American Indians was much harder, smaller and nutritious than most of the commercial corn available today. This grain was more effective in maintaining one's health, particularly strengthening the heart and blood vessels.

During the healing stage use only corn dishes that have been cooked whole at the beginning such as whole corn dishes and traditional *masa*, *tortillas* and so on. Avoid dishes that have been ground previous to any cooking as they may cause a buildup of excess mucus.

There are five main types of corn available today:

1. *Sweet corn*—The regular corn on the cob.
2. *Dent corn*—Corn with dented kernels used for making cornmeal.
3. *Flour corn*—Starchy variety used in Latin American cooking.
4. *Flint corn*—Starchy variety used in Latin American cooking.
5. *Popcorn*.

Corn on the Cob (Boiled)

Desired number of ears of fresh corn
A pot of water
Several pinches sea salt
1 Tbsp. *umeboshi* paste

Trim away the dry, outer leaves of the corn but keep the fresher inner wrapping intact. Chop off the excess straggly husk ends and silk hairs on the top end of the corn. Put sea salt in the water and bring the big pot up to a boil. Drop the corn in and boil for about 10 minutes. Take out the corn and serve. After unhusking your individual ear of corn, you can rub *umeboshi* paste on it (as you would with butter) if you want. Strain out any leftover silk hairs in the liquid with an oil skimmer and use this liquid for soup stock.

Dried Whole Corn (Dent, Flint or Flour)

2 cups whole, dried corn
8 cups spring water
2 pinches sea salt
1 cup sifted wood ash

Wash and soak the corn overnight. Put the corn, 4 cups of water and the wood ash (no salt) in a pressure-cooker. Cook for 30–45 minutes. When the corn is done, put it into a colander or strainer. Rinse out all the ash and remove the corn skins. (If the skins aren't loose enough, cook again with more ashes for another 10 minutes.) Pressure-cook the unhulled corn for 1 hour in a clean pot with salt and 4 more cups of water. You can serve this as it is or use this as a base for other corn recipes. Serves 4–6.

Masa (Corn Dough)

4 cups whole dried, flint or flour corn

8–10 cups water initially and 8 more cups later
1 cup sifted wood ash
3–4 pinches sea salt

Follow the directions in *Dried Whole Corn* except that you use 8–10 cups of water in the beginning and 8 more cups after the corn is hulled. Take out and cool the corn. Grind it in a hand grinder (not a blender). Knead this for about 15 minutes. You can moisten it with a little water if it is too dry. If you don't use the dough immediately, store it in the refrigerator (up to a week). This is the base for many corn recipes such as *arepas*, *tortillas*, cereals, and so on.

Arepas

3 cups *masa* corn dough (see above recipe)
Boiling water
Water to help shape the dough
2–3 pinches sea salt
1 Tbsp. sesame oil
Optional: **¹⁄₂ cup roasted sesame seeds**

Knead the dough while mixing in salt and optional sesame seeds. It should feel like bread dough. If it's too dry, add a little water and if too wet, add more dough or let it sit and dry for a few minutes. Separate it into balls which you mold into English muffin shapes, except a little flatter. Boil some water, put the balls inside and remove them when they rise to the top. Heat some oil in a skillet, place the *arepas* inside, cover and cook them over a low flame for about 15–20 minutes. (Turn them over halfway through to cook the other side.) If you want, you can then slit them open and stuff them with beans and/or vegetables. Serves 4–6.

Grain Products:

During the initial healing period it is better for persons with hypoglycemia to avoid flour or refined grain products altogether. This is particularly so for any dry, roasted or baked items such as bread, crackers, granola and others. However, boiled whole grain flour products may be used occasionally for variety, including noodles (but avoiding buckwheat), *fu* and *seitan*.

Persons with diabetes may be somewhat more liberal in their use of bread and other high quality grain products.

1. Noodles are a great snack and cook up very quickly. There are several types which are now available in most natural food stores.

    A. *Soba*—Long, thin, Oriental buckwheat noodles.
        1) Buckwheat with/without wheat in varying amounts

    2) *Jinenjo soba* (contains *jinenjo* flour)
    3) *Ito soba*—Extra thin and light
    4) *Ramen*—Instant noodles

B. *Udon*—Long, Oriental wholewheat noodles
    1) Thicker than *soba* and contains wholewheat and sometimes unbleached, sifted white flour.
    2) *Somen*—Very thin wheat noodles
    3) *Ramen*—Instant noodles

C. *Pasta*—Wheat alone or in combination with other grain flours.
    1) Spaghetti
    2) Shells
    3) Spirals
    4) Elbows
    5) Ribbons
    6) Ziti
    7) Rigatoni
    8) Linguini
    9) Lasagna
   10) Alphabets, etc.

Buy these noodles, especially the *ramen* and *pasta*, from natural food stores. The *ramen* bought in Oriental shops may contain animal fats, sugar, MSG, chemicals, additives and food coloring. *Pasta* bought in a regular store usually contains eggs which are best avoided.

To cook noodles, place them in a large pot of boiling water. (Too little water causes them to clump together.) As you put them in, stir and separate the noodles with a long chopstick to prevent them from lying side by side in a parallel fashion, otherwise they will stick together. (This precaution is basically for long thin noodles such as *udon* and *soba*.)

You can keep the flame high and add a little cold water each time the pot comes to a boil until the noodles are soft (usually about 3 times). Or you can turn the flame down a bit after adding the noodles and simmer until they are cooked. The first method is preferred as the noodles come out more firm and crisp. When done, the inside is the same color as the outside. Then, drain them in a colander and immediately run cold water over them. This helps to keep them from clumping together.

Don't make them too soggy especially if you are later going to reheat or fry them. Pay special attention to the *somen* and *ito soba* as they cook up very quickly and are absolutely horrible when soft and mushy.

Add a pinch of salt when boiling pasta. (*Udon* and *soba* already contain salt so they don't need it.) The leftover noodle water can be used in soup stocks.

After *ramen* is boiled, it is generally left in the pot and the accompanying packet of dry soup ingredients is mixed in. Read what the packet contains to make sure that the contents are healthy.

Noodles in Broth

   1 pack *udon* or *soba* noodles previously boiled
   1 3″–4″ piece of *kombu*
   2 *shiitake* mushrooms, soaked and sliced
   4 cups water including *shiitake* soaking water
   ½ cube *tofu* cut into smaller cubes
   3–5 Tbsp. *tamari* soy sauce
   1–2 sheets toasted *nori*, cut into small pieces
   3 chopped scallions

Make a soup stock by bringing *kombu*, *shiitake* and water to a boil and simmering for 5 minutes. Take out the *kombu* and *shiitake*. Boil the *tofu* and take them out when they rise to the top. Add the *tamari* soy sauce and simmer for 5–7 minutes. Put in some noodles (only add what you are immediately going to eat and keep the rest aside) until they become warm, then dish them out into individual bowls. Place some *tofu*, *shiitake* slices, *nori* and scallions on top of each one, pour some broth over them and serve.

For variation:

1) Use any combination of *shiitake*, *kombu* or bonito flake soup stocks.
2) Add different kinds of sea vegetables, root or green vegetables into the broth (they can be left in once they are put in), boil them till they are soft and add the *tamari* soy sauce.
3) Add different kinds of sea vegetables, root, green, boiled, sautéed, or raw (thinly sliced) vegetables as a garnish on top. Roasted seeds, *fu* (soak and boil it in the broth previously as was done with the *tofu* above), cooked *seitan* and *tempeh*, and grated *daikon* or ginger can also be added.
4) As a general rule, you can add anything as long as there is some kind of sea vegetables present as well as some kind of pungent item in the garnish. This would include scallions, diced raw onions, chives and grated ginger or *daikon*. (They help digestion.)

Zaru Soba

Soba, previously boiled
1 Tbsp. *tamari* soy sauce
1 Tbsp. brown rice vinegar
4 Tbsps. *kombu* soup stock
Chopped scallions
Nori, toasted and cut into thin strips

Place *soba* noodles onto an individual serving plate and place a few strips of *nori* on top. (In Japan they have special individual bamboo serving "plates" which allows the *soba* to drain.) Combine *tamari* soy sauce, rice vinegar, *kombu* stock, scallions into a small bowl to make a dip for the noodles. Make a dip for each person.

Fried Noodles
(In the case of hypoglycemia, it is better to avoid using this recipe initially.)

Any kind of noodles
Diced onions
Diced celery
Diced carrots
Sesame oil
Tamari soy sauce to taste
A dash of grated ginger

Sauté all the vegetables in a skillet and simmer until they become soft. Add the noodles and *tamari* soy sauce and sauté them for another 5 minutes. Add a dash of ginger, garnish with parsley sprigs and serve.

2. *Seitan* is made from the gluten of hard whole spring or winter wheat flours (they contain the most gluten). *Seitan* is protein rich.

Seitan
(This can also be bought in natural food stores. Avoid ones that have been heavily spiced if you are healing.)

3½ lbs. whole wheat flour (spring or winter)
8–9 cups of water

Place the flour into a large stainless steel mixing bowl, gradually add the water, form a dough and knead it for 5–15 minutes until it becomes stiff and earlobe consistency.

Submerge the dough in water and let it sit for 5–10 minutes. Then knead and separate the dough in the water until the liquid is full of bran and starch.

Drain the *seitan* in a colander which you place inside a large pot. (If you want, save the soaking water, starch and bran. It can be used to thicken soups, sauces, stews, puddings and so on as well as for pancakes, waffles, and sourdough starter.) Add cold water to the pot and start to knead all the bran out of the gluten.

If this water also becomes overly branny, add fresh water. (You may save this bran water as well, if you like.) Start to take small pieces of the gluten at a time and wash the bran out of them one by one. You can run them under the tap. (Some remaining flecks of bran here and there is OK. You don't have to worry about trying to get it perfectly branless.)

When finished, separate the gluten into several pieces and drop them into a pot of boiling water until they rise to the surface. (Or you can deep-fry them until they puff up and turn golden brown. Try it this way when no longer healing. It is delicous.)

You can cook the *seitan* further if you want. Put a piece of *kombu*, *seitan*, ⅓–¼ cup *tamari* soy sauce and 6 cups of water into a pot, bring to a boil, turn flame to low, cover and simmer for about a half an hour. Eat as it is or add to other dishes including soups, salads, vegetables, stews, grains, and the like.

Seitan Stew
(This hearty stew is an example of an appropriate dish to help relieve diabetes.)

> **5 onions quartered**
> **1 rutabaga cut into 1″ chunks**
> **7–10 Brussels sprouts**
> **_Seitan_, _kombu_, _tamari_ soy sauce mixture from the above recipe**
> **Finely chopped parsley**

Take the mixture from the above recipe, place the vegetables inside, add enough water so that it is level with or just covering them, bring to a boil, cover, turn flame to low and simmer 20–30 minutes or until the vegetables are soft. Add a cup or two of the leftover *seitan* starch water (see above recipe), and stir (to prevent burning) until the stew thickens. Garnish with parsley and serve. Serves 6.

Cabbage, Carrots and *Seitan*
(This quicker dish is helpful as a replacement for animal food for people with hypoglycemia.)

> **2 cups cabbage cut into 1″ squares**
> **1 cup carrots sliced on a thin diagonal**
> **Several pieces *seitan***

Enough water to cover the vegetables halfway
3 pinches sea salt
Tamari soy sauce to taste if needed

Place all the ingredients into a pot, bring to a boil, cover, turn flame to low and simmer for 10–15 minutes until the vegetables are soft. Serves 6.

3. *Fu* is also a by-product of wheat gluten. It looks like a cracker and is packaged and available in natural food stores. You can get *fu* in flat sheets or thick rounds which are available in small or large sizes.

Chinese Cabbages/*Nori*/Flat *Fu*

2 cups Chinese cabbage cut into 1″ slices
3–4 sheets flat *fu,* soaked & cut into ¼″ slices
2 sheets toasted *nori* sliced into ½″ strips
2 pinches sea salt
Enough water to just cover

Add *fu*, Chinese cabbage, salt and water into a small pot, cover, boil and simmer until the cabbage is soft (about 10 minutes). Uncover, boil away the excess liquid, turn off the flame and add and mix in the *nori* and serve. Serves 3–4.

Fu Soup with Turnips

1 cup turnips sliced medium size
½ cup turnip greens diced small
5–6 cups *kombu* soup stock
3–5 large round *fu* soaked & sliced into quarters
2 pinches sea salt
3 tsp. puréed *miso* or 3 Tbsps. *tamari* soy sauce

Bring *kombu* stock to a boil and add the turnip greens until they soften and turn a bright green (a couple of minutes—depending on how small they are). Skim them out with an oil skimmer and put them aside for now.

Add salt, bring to a boil again, put in the turnips and *fu* and boil them until they soften. Add the *miso* or *tamari* soy sauce, simmer over a low flame for 5 minutes and serve, garnished with turnip greens. Serves 6–8.

4. Sourdough bread. When healing, it is best to abstain from baked flour products as mentioned before, but if you do crave some, natural unyeasted sourdough bread is best.

Yeast is not recommended as it can cause indigestion and weakens the intestines.

Hard spring or winter wheat flours make the best bread as they contain much gluten which helps the bread rise. Any other flour can be added in smaller proportions for a variation in taste as can any cooked grains. (Cooked grains that have already gone sour can replace the sourdough starter.)

Before making a sourdough bread, you first need to make a starter.

Sourdough Starter

1 cup whole wheat flour
1–1 ½ cups well or spring water

Put flour and water into a bowl and mix them into a thick batter or porridge-like consistency, adding more flour or water as needed. Cover with a damp towel and let it sit for 2–4 days at room temperature. When it bubbles and becomes sour, it is ready to use.

Sourdough Bread (2 Loaves)

5 cups whole wheat flour
1 cup sourdough starter (or sour *seitan* water)
2 cups water
1 tsp. sea salt

Mix the starter, water and 2½ cups (a half) of the flour, let sit uncovered in a warm place for an hour or so until it rises.

(At this point, you can save half of this batter for an ongoing starter which you can keep using, adding to and recycling every week; the longer it's been around the better the bread. If you don't want to bake one week, mix in a few spoonfuls of flour and water just to keep it going and to prevent it from spoiling. This should be stored in the refrigerator.)

Add the salt and remaining flour, form into a dough, and on a floured board, start kneading the bread, about 350–400 times. The more it is kneaded the better it will rise as the bread gets more and more elastic, glutinous and smooth. This is the secret to non-yeasted breads.

Place dough into a lightly oiled bowl, cover with a damp towel and let it sit overnight at room temperature.

The next morning, punch the dough down, knead it for a few minutes and divide it in half. Place the halves into a couple of oiled bread pans and with a knife make a lengthwise slit down the center of the tops. The slit helps to give the bread some room to grow and lets steam escape. Place them in a very warm place and let sit for another 2–3 hours or until the bread rises and the slits begin to open.

Make the slits deeper and take an oiled rubber spatula and pull the bread away from the sides of the pans. Bake at 350°–375° F. for about an hour until the bread forms a beautiful brown crust.

Insert a chopstick or fork into the bread and pull it out again. If no flour sticks to it, the bread is done. Also, when tapping the bottom, you will hear a hollow sound if the bread is finished. Remove from the pans and let the loaves cool on a bread rack for a couple of hours. Eating the bread while it's still hot may cause an upset stomach. Keep loaves in a cool, dark place, wrapped in a clean cotton cloth or towel.

Slice with a bread knife. If the bread becomes hard, you can steam the slices you want to eat for a few minutes. They then become moist and appear freshly baked.

9. Soups ━━━━━━━━━━━━━━━━━━━━━━━

Most helpful soups for regular use include:

For Both Disorders:

  Miso soup with *wakame* or *daikon* and sweet tasting vegetables
  Millet or rice soup with sweet vegetables
  Azuki soup
  Tamari broth with sweet vegetables

For Diabetes:

  Occasionally sauté vegetables for *miso* soup
  Occasionally add pieces of *mochi* to your soups

For Hypoglycemia:

  Barley/*shiitake* soup
  Light *tamari* soy sauce broth with round and leafy vegetables

Soup at the beginning of a meal prepares your digestive system for all the following dishes. Just about anything can be put into a soup. Practically all types of grains, beans and their products, vegetables, sea vegetables, and occasionally fish can be used.

Soups can be adapted seasonally (and be either warming or cooling) and can add contrast to the rest of the meal. There are some general guidelines on deciding what kind of soup to use.

In the winter, make more hearty stews and thick soups with more root vegetables, grains or beans and use more salt. In the summer make lighter soups with less ingredients and more liquid, more greens, *tofu*, and so on. Also make a greater use of clear or a light *tamari* broth soups in hot weather.

For *diabetes* and *hypoglycemia*, you can often create soups with a slightly sweet taste by using sweet vegetables such as squash, carrots, parsnips, onions and cabbage. Diabetics (not hypoglycemic persons) may occasionally sauté their vegetables in a small amount of oil before adding them to their soups for extra flavor.

Adding several pieces of *mochi* is also good for diabetics. It makes a richer soup and can give you more strength. Just cut some *mochi* into 1″–2″ squares or rectangles, dry-roast them in a skillet until they soften and puff a bit and then either add it to your soups at the very end of preparation or place 1 or 2 pieces into each individual's bowl and pour the soup over them and serve. This is especially good for *miso* or broth soups. Have this 1–2 times a week.

Care should be taken to balance the soup with the rest of the meal. Some examples are:

1. Make a bean soup for a light meal lacking in more protein-rich dishes such as beans, *tempeh*, or *natto*.
2. Make a sweet vegetable soup (squash, carrots, parsnips) if the meal is lacking this sweet taste.
3. Make a root vegetable soup if the meal is mostly greens and vice versa.
4. Make a grain soup to balance a more light meal.
5. Use finely chopped vegetables if the meal contains all big chunks and vice versa.
6. Use a color in the soup which is not represented in the meal.
7. If you are not making *miso* soup, you can add *miso* somewhere else in the meal.

Use a ladle to serve your soups. This can be kept on a plate on the counter next to the soup pot or in a bowl during the course of the meal, ready to be used whenever needed.

Especially during the first few months, it is recommended that everyday, one of your meals should contain *miso* soup (unless you have soft *miso* rice that day). Also everyday, at least one of your soups should contain sea vegetables. Garnishes are important (parsley or scallions) to balance your soups as well as for decoration.

1. *Miso soup:* *Miso* is an indispensable part of the macrobiotic diet. It gives vitality, strengthens the digestive system and blood quality, and improves your assimilation of carbohydrates. When healing, eat a small amount everyday, particularly in *miso* soup.

   Miso is very salty so care must be taken to avoid consuming too much of it at one time. To use, add a spoonful of water to a couple of tablespoons or more of *miso* and mix it in to make a purée. Then, add this to the soup (or any other dish calling for *miso*).

   Miso should be added at the end after all the ingredients have softened and generally shouldn't be boiled as otherwise many valuable healing enzymes are destroyed. However, it is important to note that the soup must be simmered for a few minutes after the *miso* is added to help assimilate it into the body. If this isn't done, tightness can arise.

   The recipes below are for *hatcho* or *mugi* (barley) *miso*.

   Basic *Miso* Soup

   > *Wakame* or *kombu*, soaked and sliced
   > Choice of vegetables

Puréed *miso*
Water
Scallion or parsley garnish

Soak *wakame* or *kombu* for 10 minutes and slice. Boil the slices in water, cutting your vegetables in the meantime. Add the vegetables to the boiling water and cook until they are soft. Dilute and purée the *miso* with some of the soup water, turn down the flame, and when the soup has stopped bubbling, gently add and stir the *miso* purée into the soup. Simmer for 2–4 minutes and serve with a garnish. It is important that the soup be light and energetic by keeping your vegetables fresh and crispy, being careful not to overcook them.

Wakame and *Daikon Miso* Soup

½ cup *wakame*, washed, soaked & sliced
½ cup *daikon* cut any way you want
4 cups spring water
1½ Tbsps. puréed *miso*
2 scallions sliced

Follow the recipe for *Basic Miso Soup*. Serves 6.

Fig. 10 *Daikon*

Squash, Onion *Miso* Soup

½ cup sliced onions
½ cup cubed buttercup or Hokkaido squash
4 cups spring water
1½ Tbsps. puréed *miso*
Several sprigs of parsley garnish

Place onions and squash into a pot, just barely covering them with water and boil and simmer until they become soft. Add the rest of the water and bring to a boil again. Turn the flame to low, purée the *miso* with a spoonful of soup water and when the water has stopped bubbling, add the *miso* and simmer another 3–5 minutes. Serves 6.

2. *Clear broth or tamari soy sauce soup:* This is a light soup which is very appealing in the hot summer months or when the rest of the meal is more heavy. A stronger *tamari* broth is very good as a standard supper soup or for noodles.

For a clear soup, make a soup stock (a few examples are listed at the end of this chapter) and add the vegetables and some form of salt. You may . . .

A. keep the clear color of the soup stock by using sea salt (a pinch or two for every cup of liquid),

B. make it darker with 2–3 tablespoons of *tamari* soy sauce for every four cups of liquid (most often used),

C. or use 1 tablespoon of *umeboshi* paste or 2–3 tablespoons of *umeboshi* vinegar or 2–3 *umeboshi* plums for every 4 cups of liquid. This gives an attractive pink coloring to your soup.

Tofu, Watercress, *Tamari* Broth Soup

1 cube fresh *tofu* cut into smaller cubes
1 bunch watercress, washed
½ carrot cut into very thin matchsticks
1 onion cut into very thin half moons
4 cups soup stock
2–3 Tbsps. *tamari* soy sauce

Bring the soup stock up to a boil, drop in the watercress for 2 seconds and take them out again, leaving them aside to drain for the time being. Add the carrots and onions until they are soft. Then add the *tamari* and *tofu* (until it rises to the top) and simmer over a low flame for 3–5 minutes. Dish the soup out into individual bowls and garnish with the boiled watercress (which you may chop into more bite-size slices if you desire). Serves 4.

3. *Grain and bean soups:* You can pressure-cook these soups first or just boil them gently for a longer time.

A. To boil, layer the vegetables into a pot. Place the more yin vegetables on the bottom and more yang ones on the top (except for greens which are added later and placed on top of everything). Then add the grains or beans and enough water just to *Barely* cover everything. Bring to a slow boil, adding more water as the grains or beans expand. You can place a heat deflector underneath to help prevent burning. This is the same method used in boiling beans (see *Beans and Bean Products* chapter) except that instead of boiling away the excess liquid in the end, we add more to make it soupy. The salt and/or *miso* or *tamari* are added after the grain or bean has softened (simmer another 3–10 minutes after the seasoning is added). More water can be added if the consistency is too thick.

Soaking the bean or grain beforehand shortens the cooking time. You can also use previously cooked grains or beans. In this case, first boil the vegetables until they are soft before adding them. Also, you may sauté the vegetables and/or roast the grains or beans beforehand. An optional piece of *kombu* may be added in the bottom of the pot.

Millet/Squash Soup

Follow directions in the *Millet and Squash* recipe in the *Grains and Grain Products* chapter, except add more water. Other sweet vegetables may also be used. Rice may be substituted for the millet.

Barley *Shiitake* Soup

1 cup barley, soaked 6–8 hours or overnight
3 *shiitake* mushrooms soaked a few minutes
2 pinches sea salt
5–6 cups spring water
A few drops *tamari* soy sauce to taste

Fig. 11 *Shiitake* mushroom

Pressure-cook all ingredients for 40–45 minutes. Let the pressure come down completely, uncover, bring to a boil again, add *tamari* soy sauce, turn the flame to low, place a heat deflector underneath and simmer for another 10 minutes. Serves 4.

B. Pressure-cooking. The grains or beans are first pressure-cooked. The cover is then taken off. The salt (especially in the case of beans as some grain dishes can take salt from the beginning), *tamari* soy sauce or *miso*, and perhaps some vegetables are then added. Then all this is simmered, up to 20–30 minutes longer, depending on the dish.

Azuki Bean/Onion/Rutabaga Soup

1 cup *azuki* beans
½ cup diced onions
½ cup diced rutabagas
5–6 cups water
½ tsp. sea salt
1 strip *kombu*, 4″–5″
Several sprigs of parsley garnish

Layer the *kombu*, onions, rutabagas and then the *azuki* beans on top. Add water and pressure-cook, simmering for 45 minutes after the pressure has come up. Then let the pressure come down, remove the cover, add the salt, simmer over a low flame for 10 minutes and serve with parsley.

4. *Soup stocks:* These soup stocks can be used for any of the above types of soups. They are particularly good for the clear, *miso* and vegetable soups.

Kombu Soup Stock

1 piece *kombu*, 3″–6″
5–6 cups of water

If there is any dust on the *kombu*, wipe it off with a clean, damp cloth. Leave the white powder on. Bring the *kombu* and water to a boil, simmer about 3 minutes and remove the *kombu*. It can be reused for another stock (boil it longer the next time to get more out of it), added to another dish, or sliced and used in this one.

Other variations:

a) **4 *shiitake* mushrooms, simmer 5–6 minutes**
b) **2 Tbsps. bonito fish flakes, 3–4 minutes**
c) **Any combination of *kombu, shiitake* and bonito**
d) **Odd and ends of vegetables such as onion skins, cabbage cores, roots, tops and so on. Wash well, boil 5 minutes, and discard or use for compost**
e) **Other sea vegetabes like *wakame* and dulse**
f) **Dry-roast grains such as rice, sweet rice, millet, buckwheat or barley until a nutty fragrance is emitted and use for stock. Simmer 4–5 minutes.**
g) **_Chirimen iriko_ (small, whole dried fish available in natural and Oriental food stores).**
    Boil 2 Tbsps. for 3–4 minutes.
h) **Leftover liquid from boiling vegetables**
i) **Water leftover from cooking beans**
j) **Diluted water leftover from cooking *seitan*.**

10. Vegetables ━━━━━━━━━━

Most helpful dishes for regular use include:

For Both: Disorders

> *Nishime* style sweet-tasting vegetables, especially with *kombu*
>   (use lighter seasoning for hypoglycemia)
> Boiled or steamed leafy greens
> Dried *daikon* with *kombu*
> Any cooked dish with round, sweet-tasting vegetables
>   (onions, cabbage, squash, etc.)

For Diabetes:

> Pressure-cooked sweet or root vegetables
> Baked squash (in season)
> *Kinpira* (with oil)
> Any long time pickles (over a week)

For Hypoglycemia:

> "Water sautéed" cabbage or other sweet or leafy vegetables
> Boiled *daikon*, turnip, carrot or dandelion with their greens
> Boiled or pressed salad
> Any light, short time pickles (less than a week)

As much as possible, you should get organically grown, chemical-free vegetables. Besides being healthier for you, they are more delicious. Organic farmers put much care and attention into producing food that benefits both mankind and the planet. Also avoid dull colored, limp, yellow leaved, soft spotted and wrinkled items as they are either too old, spoiled, dried up and/or don't have much vitality.

Choose locally grown produce as often as possible, though in the north during the winter you would have to rely more on southern grown ones. Prepackaged items tend to spoil more quickly. Stay away from canned and frozen foods. They have no energy and/or have added salt, sugar and preservatives, all of which are best avoided. Also, be careful not to buy waxed items.

At home, immediately remove any yellow leaves and spoiled parts of your vegetables before you store them. This helps to preserve the rest for a longer time. When storing vegetables in the refrigerator, keep them in a paper bag; this allows them to absorb extra moisture and thereby retards spoilage. A plastic bag retains water, doesn't allow your vegetables to breath and causes them to grow soggy and spoil more quickly. Keep your vegetables separated from your fruits for better preservation.

Don't wash your vegetables until you are ready to use them. Any soil left on them helps to keep them longer. When you do wash them, particularly your leafy greens, it helps to submerge them in a big bowl of water. Swish them around a little bit and wash each leaf individually. This automatically separates and loosens the sand, soil and dirt which settles to the bottom of the bowl, as the greens stay afloat. This is much more effective and easier than just trying to rinse them under the tap. Roots can be scrubbed gently with a vegetable brush (*tawashi*) to remove the soil but make sure to keep the skin on. (If you are dealing with organic vegetables, you don't have to peel your cucumbers, carrots and so on as they are not sprayed, or covered with wax. The skins contain many nourishing nutrients.)

To wash leeks, cut them in half lengthwise and clean out all the dirt trapped in between the layers of leaves. The soil usually collects in the section where the colors change from white to green.

Always use cold water when you clean as hot water washes out many vitamins and minerals. Wash vegetables quickly. Soaking for any length of time also depletes valuable nutrients.

Within one dish, cut your vegetables uniformly for even cooking. Within a meal have a variety of different sizes represented in several dishes— smaller for sautéed items and bigger chunks for stews, for example.

Save the tops and roots of vegetables as much as you can. They can be cleaned, chopped very finely and incorporated into your vegetable dishes. You can also leave them uncut and use them in a soup stock. Using the whole plant helps to create a balance in your system.

I recommend the square, Japanese vegetable knives (see *cookware* section) for cutting your vegetables. They are very handy, flexible and easy to use. With these knives, don't cut straight down or use them like a saw. Starting with the front tip or edge, gently slide the length of the blade across your vegetables in one smooth stroke. *Important: Always Keep Your Fingertips Curled Underneath So That Your Knuckles Show When You're Cutting*. This helps to protect them from accidental cuts and slips and you also get a better grip on the vegetable as well.

There are several cutting styles to choose from. Here is a partial listing.

1) **Round slices.**	7) **Matchsticks.**
2) **Diagonal slices.**	8) **Shavings.**
3) **Triangular shapes.**	9) **Cubes, dicing and mincing.**
4) **Rectangles.**	10) **Wedge slices**
5) **Half-moons.**	11) **Slicing cabbages.**
6) **Quarters.**	12) **Slicing big leafy greens.**

Fig. 12   Round slices

Fig. 13   Diagonal slices

Fig. 14   Triangular shapes

Fig. 15   Rectangles

Fig. 16   Half-moons

Fig. 17   Quarters

Fig. 18   Matchsticks

Fig. 19   Shavings

84

Fig. 20   Cubes, dicing and mincing

Fig. 21   Wedge slices

Fig. 22   Slicing cabbages

Fig. 23 Slicing big leafy greens

Along the veins

Slicing greens

The stem

Include a variety of different kinds of vegetables (roots, greens, ground and sea vegetables, for example) in a meal as well as an assortment of textures and colors. Also, use a variety of cooking styles. Here are some of the main methods that we use.

1. *Boiling methods:*   There are two main styles: quick, short time and slow, longer time boiling. You can have some kind of boiled vegetables at nearly every meal.

    A. Quick boiling (blanching): The best way to cook your leafy green vegetables. Fill a pot with 1–2 inches of water which you bring to a rolling boil. Dip in your vegetables and take them out quickly. An oil skimmer lifts them up very easily. Drain the vegetables in a colander. (Place a plate underneath to catch any liquid that drips out. This water can be put back into the pot.)

    The main point in this style is to cook in as short a time as possible, retaining crispness and bright colors. For example, watercress can be taken out after 15–30 seconds. Others take a little longer, in varying degrees, but not that much more. Kale, mustard greens, collard greens, cabbage, chinese cabbage, broccoli, cauliflower, celery and others can be used.

    A pinch of salt in the water helps to retain bright colors (but leave it out for bitter vegetables such as watercress and mustard greens as then the bitterness stays inside as well).

You can also cook root vegetables in this way but you have to cut them into very thin slices. You can boil them for a slightly longer time than you would with greens.

If you want to boil several different vegetables, do them one by one. Start with the lighter tasting varieties like the cabbages and end with more strong tasting ones like mustard greens so that the flavor of the latter won't effect the flavor of the former. Each vegetable's distinct individuality should be maintained.

You can use the leftover boiling water as a base for a soup. Or you can add some *kuzu* to it (2 teaspoons for 1 cup water) to thicken it into a sauce to pour over your vegetables. To do this: first dilute the *kuzu* in a small amount of water. Turn the flame to low underneath the boiled water and pour the *kuzu* in. Stir and simmer until the liquid turns clear. Add a little *tamari* soy sauce or *umeboshi* paste to taste and pour this over your boiled vegetables.

Two recipe examples:

Boiled Broccoli and Onions

1 bunch broccoli
3 onions, sliced into thin half moons
4 cups spring water
1 pinch sea salt

Separate the broccoli flowers from the stems. Cut the stems into thin matchsticks. Bring the water and salt to a boil. Put in and boil the broccoli stems until they are soft. Scoop them out with an oil skimmer and drain them in a colander. Then boil the broccoli flowers until they turn a bright green. Scoop out and drain them. Boil the onions until they are soft and scoop and drain them. Place all the vegetables onto a serving plate, arranging them into a pretty design and serve.

Boiled Salad

Chinese cabbage cut into 1″ slices
1 bunch of watercress
Carrots cut into matchsticks
4 cups spring water
Roasted sesame seeds

Quickly and separately boil the Chinese cabbage, carrots, and watercress (only until it turns a bright green). Drain each of them and mix them together into a serving bowl. Sprinkle the roasted sesame seeds on top.

B.   Slow, longer time boiling: This style is basically for root vegetables such as *daikon*, carrots, onions, lotus root, burdock and so
on, as well as squash. This style gives a calming but strong and
healing energy.

One or two pieces of *kombu* are usually placed in the bottom of
the pot to help prevent the vegetables from burning, to add extra
minerals and flavor, and to help harmonize all the ingredients
together.

The vegetables are then layered on top of the *kombu*, with the
more yin ones on the bottom and the more yang ones on the top.
The yin rising energy meets the yang descending energy and the
dish is better integrated.

If the vegetables are fairly dry, put in enough water to just
cover them. If they are fresh and more watery, cover them with
water only halfway. Add a pinch of salt, cover the pot, bring
everything up to a boil, turn the flame to low and simmer for
about 20 minutes or until soft. The time depends on the type,
quality and slice sizes of the vegetables used. Don't mix or stir
the vegetables. When the vegetables are soft, add some *tamari*
soy sauce for more flavor and simmer another 5 minutes. *Shiitake*
mushrooms, dried *tofu*, *tempeh* and *seitan* may also be added to
this dish.

Cauliflower, Carrots and Onions

> 1 cauliflower, separate the individual flowers
> 2 carrots cut into triangular wedges
> 3 onions, quartered
> 1 piece *kombu*
> 1 pinch sea salt
> Enough water to cover the vegetables halfway
> *Tamari* soy sauce to taste

Place *kombu* in the bottom of the pot. Add the other ingredients
in this order from the bottom up, cauliflower, onions and carrots.
Add water and salt, cover, and follow the above directions.
Serves 2–3.

Dried *Daikon* and *Kombu*

> 1 cup dried *daikon* soaked until soft (10 minutes)
> 1 piece *kombu* 4″–5″, washed & soaked 10 minutes
> Enough water to just cover them
> *Tamari* soy sauce to taste

Cut the *kombu* into thin, lengthwise, matchstick-like strips. Put it into a pot and place the *daikon* on top. (Dried *daikon* comes in shredded strips and can be found in natural food stores.) Add enough water to just cover the *daikon*. You can use the soaking water but if the *daikon* is too dark, discard its water. Add fresh water if you don't have enough. Cover the pot, bring it to a boil, lower the flame and simmer for 30–40 minutes until the *kombu* becomes soft. Add *tamari* soy sauce to taste, boil away the excess liquid and serve. Serves 2–3.

2. *Nishime style:* This is a very medicinal form of cooking using a minimal amount of water. For this you need a heavy pot with a heavy lid or some cookware specifically designed for waterless cooking.

Kombu at the bottom of the pot helps to prevent burning as well as adding extra minerals and taste.

Root vegetables such as carrots, *daikon*, turnips, burdock, lotus root, onions and hard winter squash (acorn, buttercup or Hokkaido), cabbage and *shiitake* mushrooms are normally used. They are usually cut into 2″ chunks (except for burdock which is cut about half the size or smaller) and layered on top of the *kombu* from yin to yang (yin on the bottom). Squash dissolves and loses its shape if cooked for a long time, so you may add it a little later on.

To cook, soak a piece of *kombu* until it's soft, cut it into 1″ squares and place it in the bottom of a pot. Add enough water just to cover the *kombu* if the vegetables are fresh and watery. If they are more dry or if using burdock or lotus root, add enough water to cover the vegetables halfway. Put in the vegetables and sprinkle a small amount of sea salt or *tamari* soy sauce over them.

Cover, set the flame on high until a steam is produced. Then lower the flame and let the vegetables simmer peacefully for 15–20 minutes. If water should evaporate during cooking, add a little more to the bottom of the pot if it is necessary to prevent burning.

When all the vegetables have softened, add a few more drops of *tamari* soy sauce to taste.

Then, replace the cover and cook over a low flame for 2–5 minutes more. After turning off the flame, remove the cover and let the vegetables sit for about 2 minutes. Serve the juice along with the vegetables as it is very delicious.

Squash, Cabbage, Onion and *Kombu*

1 large buttercup squash cut into 2″ chunks
½ head of cabbage cut into 2″ squares
5 onions quartered
1 piece *kombu*, 6″–8″, soaked and sliced into 1″ pieces

2 pinches sea salt
Tamari **soy sauce to taste**
Enough water to just cover the *kombu*

Follow the above directions. Serves 4–6.

A few variation examples:

1) **Carrots, cabbage, burdock,** *kombu*
2) *Daikon, shiitake* **mushrooms,** *kombu*
3) **Turnip,** *shiitake* **mushrooms,** *kombu*
4) **Carrots, lotus root, burdock,** *kombu*
5) **Onion,** *kombu*
6) *Daikon,* **lotus root, dried** *tofu, kombu*
7) **Parsnips, onions,** *kombu*

Turnip/Turnip Leaves

Turnip roots and leaves
1 piece *kombu*, **3″–6″, soaked and sliced**
Miso **or** *tamari* **soy sauce to taste**
Enough water to just cover the *kombu*

Wash and very finely slice the roots and leaves. Put the *kombu* in a pot with enough water just to cover it. Add the roots, cover and cook with a high steam for 10 minutes or longer. Towards the end, add the leaves, *miso* or *tamari* soy sauce to taste and simmer for another 2–4 minutes.

Other variations (finely chopped):

1) *Daikon* **and its leaves or tops**
2) **Carrot and its tops (slice tops extra fine)**
3) **Radish and its tops**
4) **Dandelion root and leaves**

3. *Sautéing:* There are two ways to sauté: with or without oil, using water as a substitute. When limiting your use of oil, you can use the water-sautéing method as often as you like.

With oil. It is best to use only sesame oil (particularly the dark or roasted variety) and to spread it onto the bottom of a heated pan rather than to pour it in. Put your oil into a cast-iron skillet (don't use too much, perhaps 1 tablespoon for 8 pepople) and heat it up with a medium high flame. When the oil seems warm, test it by dropping in one slice of a vegetable. If the oil sizzles, then it is ready and you can put in the rest of the ingredients.

When "water sautéing," simply add a tablespoon or two of water as needed in cooking to prevent burning.

As an option, if using onions, many people like to sauté them first. I find that first sautéing them till they become translucent before putting in the next vegetable (move the onions on top of them) makes a very sweet dish.

You can either add the different kinds of vegetables one by one, starting with the ones that take the longest time to cook and ending with the faster cooking ones, or you can cut them so that the different types of vegetables will cook at the same rate (soft vegetables in larger slices, tougher ones in thinner slices) and layer them from yin to yang (yin in the bottom).

After putting in the vegetables, add a pinch or two of sea salt. Salt brings out the natural sweetness, draws out the water and helps to soften the vegetables quicker (it has the opposite effect on grains and beans and is therefore added later on in their case). Gently stir from time to time (with a wooden spoon or cooking chopsticks) to prevent burning.

After about 5 minutes you can turn the flame to low, cover (unless you are working with really watery items such as Chinese cabbage or *tofu*) and simmer until the vegetables are soft; the time it takes depends on what you're cooking and the size of your slices. You may need to add a little water to avoid burning, especially when cooking with something like burdock. Add a little *tamari* soy sauce (and some grated ginger if you wish) at the end for more flavor and simmer another 2–3 minutes. Uncover and boil away any excess water if there is any.

Any vegetable can be sautéed (cut your root vegetables into very thin slices or shavings) as can *tofu* and *tempeh*.

Two recipe examples:

Kinpira Carrots, Burdock
(This dish is very strengthening and can be used once or twice a week for those with diabetes. When preparing this dish for persons who have hypoglycemia, substitute the oil with a little water.)

1 cup shaved burdock
2 cups shaved carrots
Dark sesame oil (optional)
A pinch sea salt
***Tamari* soy sauce to taste**
***Optional:* ½ tsp. grated ginger**
Water, if needed to prevent burning
A few parsley sprigs

Heat oil in a skillet, add carrots, burdock and salt and follow the above directions. Add a small amount of water if needed to prevent burning. Garnish with the parsley. Serves 4–6.

Fig. 24 Burdock

Sautéed Vegetables
(This type of lighter dish using some of the "occasional use" vegetables is very nice for variety and freshness.)

> 5 celery stalks cut into very thin diagonal slices
> ½ cup fresh corn kernels off the cob
> 1 cake *tofu* cut into 1″ cubes
> 5 radishes cut into thin rounds
> Dark sesame oil or 1–2 Tbsps. water
> A pinch sea salt
> *Tamari* soy sauce to taste
> A dash of grated ginger

Heat oil or water in a skillet, sauté *tofu*, then celery and corn, adding a pinch of sea salt. Towards the end, add the radishes. Don't cover. Boil off any excess water. Add soy sauce to taste and simmer another 3 minutes. Add a dash of ginger and serve. Serves 3–4.

4. *Pressure-cooking:* This is good for big chunks of root vegetables and squash (but don't cook greens this way). Use this style as often as you wish as long as you make sure that you are also making fresher vegetables such as salad and boiled or steamed greens to balance all the pressure-cooking that you will be doing with your grains and beans. After the pressure comes up, carrots and onions may be done in 5 minutes and big chunks of lotus root and burdock in 15–20 minutes.

After putting your ingredients into the pressure-cooker, add enough water to just cover the bottom of the pot (maybe ½″–1″). Add salt, cover, bring to pressure over a medium high flame. When up, turn the flame to low and simmer until done. Rinse the pot under cold water if you want to bring the pressure down quickly. (Don't uncover the pot until it's completely down.)

Buttercup or Hokkaido Squash

1 Buttercup or Hokkaido squash
1 pinch sea salt
Enough water to cover the bottom of the pot

Scrub the dirt off with a vegetable brush and rinse the squash in cold water. Cut away all the crusty, flesh colored growths on the skin (found on buttercups). Cut the squash open and remove the seeds. (You can save them for your garden or as seeds for eating.) Slice the squash into big chunks and place them in the pressure-cooker with sea salt. Cover and follow the above directions, simmering for 10 minutes after the pressure comes up. Serves 3–4.

Fig. 25 Buttercup squash and Butternut squash

5. *Steaming:* You can use this method fairly often if you like. To steam, add ½″–1″ of cold water in the bottom of a pot, insert a steamer, place your vegetable inside with a pinch of salt, cover, and bring the water to a boil. Then steam for 3–10 minutes or more until your vegetable is soft.

Good for any kind of vegetable and makes a nice variation to the boiled method. Be careful not to overcook them. Remove them while they're still crisp and brightly colored.

Steam each kind of vegetable separately unless you are going to serve them mixed together and they take the same amount of time to cook. When you put in a new vegetable, let the water cool a bit so that it gets cooked more evenly. If you want to keep their bright color, run the vegetables under cold water and don't cover them until they cool off. The leftover water can be used as soup stock or sauce (just like the boiling water). Steaming is a great way to heat up leftovers, especially rice.

Steamed *Daikon* and Kale

1 cup *daikon* cut into very thin matchsticks
Several leaves of kale
1 pinch sea salt

Separate the stems of the kale from the leafy part. Slice the stems into very thin diagonal slices. Slice the leaves into ¼″ strips. Follow the above directions and steam the *daikon*, kale leaves and kale stems separately for 5–10 minutes or until soft. Then combine them into a nice arrangement on a serving plate and serve. Serves 3–4.

Fig. 26 Kale

6. *Salad:* There are three types of salads.

A. *Boiled salad:* Refer to the section on boiled vegetables for directions and an example. This can be taken several times a week.

B. *Pressed salad:* This can generally be eaten every two or three days. The vegetables are raw but pressing them with salt helps to yangize them. However, it may still be a little too yin for frequent use in cold weather for persons with severe diabetes. In this case, take this only once a week.

    To prepare, cut your vegetables into very thin slices or shred them and put them in a pickle press with sea salt for one or more hours. Drain off the excess water, wash off the excess salt and serve.

If you don't have a pickle press you can put your vegetables in a bowl and cover them with a plate. Put a rock or some kind of weight (such as a large glass jar filled with water) on top of the plate and press.

Pressed Salad

3 turnips cut into very thin matchsticks
2 tsps. sea salt or 1½ Tbsps. *umeboshi* juice.

Mix ingredients into a pickle press and follow the above directions. If it is too salty, you can quickly rinse it off in cold water before serving. Serves about 3.

C. *Regular raw salad:*   Persons trying to alleviate diabetes should avoid this for awhile, perhaps several months. Otherwise, this is recommended about once or twice a week and more during the hot summer months.

You can use the usual vegetables such as lettuce, cucumbers, sprouts, carrots, onions, celery, parsley, etc., but avoid peppers, potatoes, tomatoes, eggplants and mushrooms. (You can also add roasted sesame and pumpkin seeds, wholewheat bread croutons, cooked chickpeas, pinto beans, rice, bulghur, couscous, noodles, macaroni, *wakame*, dried dulse and cooked *hijiki, arame, tofu, tempeh,* and *seitan.* Of course, your combinations have to be tasteful. Obviously, not all those ingredients are compatible with each other.)

Wakame Salad

1 cup *wakame* (Wash, soak 10 minutes, boil 2–3 minutes, rinse in cold water, drain & slice into 1″ pieces.)
1 iceberg lettuce cut into bite-size pieces
1 cucumber sliced into thin rounds.
1 Tbsp. *umeboshi* paste

Peel off the cucumber skin if it is waxed. Cut off the ends and with sea salt, rub them in a circular motion against the ends of the main body of the cucumber. This helps to draw out any bitterness if there is any. Rinse off the salt and slice. Mix with the *wakame*, lettuce and *umeboshi* paste. Serves 3.

Pinto Bean Salad

½ cup cooked pinto beans
½ cup cooked fresh corn kernels
1 diced onion
1 cucumber cut into little cubes
5 sliced radishes

Mix all the ingredients together and add your preferred dressing (see *Seasonings, Condiments and Dressings* chapter).

7. *Baked:* This method takes a long time to cook but it gives strength and extra flavor. It's best to bake once in a while for variety rather than on a daily basis.

This style is good for squashes and root vegetables. You can leave them whole (burdock should be sliced) or cut them in half or in chunks.

You can bake them with or without oil, using a casserole dish or a cookie sheet covered with foil. If your vegetables are fresh and juicy you may not need to add water, especially if you oil the sheet or dish and have a good cover. If you don't use oil, add just a little water to cover the surface. If your vegetables are more dried out or are tough, add about a ¼"–½" of water. Adding a dash of salt helps to draw out the water.

Place your vegetables, salt, water and/or oil into a dish or onto a sheet, cover, turn to 350°–375° F. and bake for 45–60 minutes, or until they're soft. Towards the end you can uncover, let any extra water (if any) evaporate, add *tamari* soy sauce, *miso* or some sauce to taste and simmer for another 5 minutes or so until done.

You can bake squash whole and uncovered on an oiled cookie sheet (with stuffing inside if you prefer). Or you can cut it in half and place the halves on the sheet (again uncovered) with the inside facing down. Don't forget to take out the seeds.

Baked Root Vegetables

    1 buttercup or Hokkaido squash cut into 1″ cubes
    2 burdocks cut into diagonal slices
    3 onions quartered
    1 strip *kombu*
    1 pinch sea salt
    ¾ cup water

Place the *kombu* in the bottom of a casserole dish. Put all the vegetables on top of it, each in its own little corner of the dish. Add salt, water and cover. Bake at 350°–375° F. for 45–60 minutes or until soft. Uncover, add *tamari* soy sauce to taste, let some of the water evaporate, remove from the stove and serve. Serves about 4.

8. *Pickles:* Pickles are an extremely important addition to your diet. Have a small amount on the side at every meal or at least once a day and eat them with your grains. They aid in digestion, strengthen the flora in your intestines, stimulate your appetite and add zest to the meal.

Always use fresh, firm, and crisp vegetables for making pickles. Also, it is imperative that the vegetables, containers and anything else you use be thoroughly cleaned. You don't want any unknown substances interacting with the pickling process. For tougher vegetables, it is helpful to quickly blanch them in boiling water before pickling them.

Pickling time ranges from a couple of hours to several months. The main time factors are the size of your vegetables and the amount of salt you use. Small, thinly sliced pieces can be pickled very quickly where as large, thick or whole pieces take a long time. Long-time pickling requires more salt to retard the fermenting process. You can dip your vegetables in hot boiling water before you pickle them if you choose, especially with largely sliced and/or hard vegetables. This takes out the raw flavor and brings out a sweeter taste.

A lot of experimentation may be needed to get the feel of the right amount of salt to use. If the vegetables spoil before they pickle and/or not much water comes out (for methods that require that it does), then there isn't enough salt. If too much salt is added, the pickles will become too salty and any other flavor that the vegetables may have had will be covered up. To take out excess salt, rinse out or soak your pickles for a little while before you eat them.

If mold starts to form anywhere, remove it immediately so that the rest of the contents won't be affected.

Cover the whole thing with a cheesecloth. It helps to keep dirt and dust out of the pickles while letting the air circulate and enabling them to breathe. (Don't cover with an airtight lid.)

There are four main types of pickling methods that we usually use.

A. *Pressed pickles:* You can make them quickly, in a couple of hours, or you can make them in several weeks.

1) *Quick pickles:* When pickling for a few hours up to a day or two, you can use a pickle press. But since most of them are made out of plastic, it's not safe to use them for a longer period of time as the poisonous toxic substances in them will start to seep into the vegetables. If you don't have a press or if you want to use something safer, you can take a small glass bowl and find a saucer that fits into it. It should cover the inside as much as possible but still remain loose so that water can escape over the sides. For a weight, you can use a glass jar full of water, grains or beans or some clean stones.

Soft, watery vegetables like thinly sliced cucumbers and very thin matchstick *daikon* strips can be done in 2–3 hours. Other pickles can be made in the morning and be either eaten for dinner or left for 2–3 days longer. Some (like harder, less watery vegetables like turnips) may need the extra time. Again, it mostly depends on the size of the pieces.

The vegetables have to be cut into really thin slices or shredded for this method. (An exception is mustard greens which can be made whole and cut when you want to eat them. Mix the salt in well and wait 2–3 days.) Chinese cabbage, red and white cabbage, *daikon* and its greens, turnips and its greens, celery, radishes, onions, cucumbers and bok-choy are good to use. For best results, use only one kind of vegetable at a time. You can add a strip of *kombu* (perhaps 3″–6″ long for two cups of vegetables) for extra minerals and a different flavor. Soak the *kombu* until it's soft, slice it into thin strips and put it underneath the vegetables. Grated ginger can be added if you wish.

For 2 cups of vegetables add about 1–2 teaspoons of salt. Mix them together thoroughly. The salt can be substituted with 2–4 teaspoons of *umeboshi* vinegar, paste, or plums and/or *shiso* leaves. You can also use 2–4 tablespoons of *tamari* soy sauce. Water will start to rise above the saucer or pressure plate. If there is a lot you can take a little out but always leave some of it covering the plate. Cover with a cheesecloth (not necessary if using a press of course) and wait till it's all done.

Onion Pickles

> **2 cups of thinly sliced onions**
> **2–4 Tbsps. *tamari* soy sauce**

Pickle the onions in soy sauce following the above directions. If the onions were cut really thinly it will be done in 2 hours. You can also eat them the next day.

2) *Longer time pressed pickles:* A wooden keg or ceramic crock are good containers to use for this. A heavy stone or large jar filled with water is placed on top of a plate or a wooden disc which fits inside for pressure. Cover the whole thing with a cheesecloth and place in a cool dark place. Check regularly for mold and remove it immediately if any appears. Sauerkraut is made this way. Below is a sample recipe.

Pressed *Daikon* Pickles

> **4–5 *daikons***
> **½ cup sea salt**

Wash, dry completely and cut the *daikons* into several lengthwise strips. Place a layer of salt in a crock or wooden keg. Then a layer of *daikon*. Then a layer of salt. Alternate until all the *daikon* is in. Salt should be the last layer. Place a weight on top, cover with cheesecloth and press for 1–2 weeks or more following the above directions. Chinese cabbage (separate all the leaves and make the layers with them), carrots, turnips, *daikon* greens, and so on can also be made this way.

B. *Brine pickles:*   To make this pickle, tightly stuff some vegetables into a glass jar. Boil some kind of a brine mixture, let it cool off and pour it into the jar, filling it up. Cover the top with cheesecloth which you can fasten down with a rubber band and pickle for several days. When done, store them in a refrigerator. This is how dill pickles are made. Beside cucumbers, you can use onions, turnips, rutabagas, *daikon*, carrots, broccoli, cauliflower, cabbages, greens and so on.

There are several kinds of brine that you can choose to use, examples of which I have presented below. You can use a soup stock if you want. You can add ginger, *kombu*, *shiitake* mushrooms, lemon juice and rinds, *shiso* leaves, grated raw apple and so on, for extra flavor. Some *ame* rice syrup can be boiled and dissolved into the brine (good with the *tamari* based one) for a sweet taste.

Onion-Cucumber Pickles (Salt Based Brine)

> 3 lbs. pickling cucumbers
> 2 onions quartered
> 12 cups spring water
> 1/3–1/2 cup sea salt
> 3 sprigs fresh or dry dill (*optional*)

Bring water and salt to a boil. Turn the flame to medium low and simmer until all the salt has dissolved. Cool this off. Wash and place cucumbers, onions and dill into a glass jar. Pour the cooled liquid inside and fill it up to the top. Cover with a cheesecloth and keep in a dark location for 3–4 days. When finished, keep it in the refrigerator.

Lotus Root, *Shiitake* and *Wakame* (*Tamari* Based Brine)

> Enough thin lotus root rounds to fill a quart jar
> 1/4 cup soaked *wakame* cut into 1″ slices
> 2 *shiitake* mushrooms
> 1 cup *tamari* soy sauce

2 cups spring water
1 Tbsp. grated ginger

Bring the *shiitake* and water to a boil. Add the *tamari* soy sauce and bring to a boil again. Turn flame to medium low and simmer for 5 minutes. Remove from the stove, add the ginger and then cool off the liquid. Wash, slice and place the lotus root, and *wakame* into a quart jar. Add the cooled off liquid and mushrooms into the jar over the vegetables. Cover with a cheesecloth and let sit 3–4 days.

Cauliflower and Radish Pickles (*Umeboshi* Based Brine)

Enough cauliflower pieces to fill a glass quart jar
5 radishes cut in half
2 cups water
1 cup *umeboshi* vinegar
5 *shiso* leaves

Place cauliflower and radishes into a jar. Mix the water, *umeboshi* vinegar and *shiso* leaves together and pour them into the jar over the vegetables. Cover with cheesecloth and let sit 3–4 days.

C. *Miso pickles:* Miso pickles are especially helpful for recovering good digestive strength. They are simple to make. Just quickly blanch your vegetables in boiling water and then submerge and surround them totally in *miso*. This is used for root vegetables such as carrots, burdock, *daikon*, turnips, parsnips and ginger. Broccoli stems make great pickles as well. Greens are too watery.

The vegetables have to be dried out until you can band them like rubber before you put them into the *miso*. Otherwise, the *miso* will get too watery and the pickling won't work.

Pickling time depends on the vegetables you use and the size of your slices. Very thin ones can pickle in 3–4 days, up to a week. Whole vegetables with slits in their sides can take 1–2 weeks, thick slices about 3 months and whole vegetables (unslitted) can be left in the *miso* up to a year. Just make sure they are totally submerged (top, bottom, and sides). You don't need to use any pressure.

When the pickles are done, just take them out, rinse them off, slice them and eat them.

Broccoli Stem *Miso* Pickles

Broccoli Stems
A container of *miso*

Take your leftover broccoli stems. Peel them unless the skins are soft, quickly blanch them in boiling water and submerge them into the *miso* for 1–2 weeks, depending on how thick they are. You can leave the skins on if you like. The pickling time will be much longer then, maybe a month or more. Cover with a cheesecloth and keep in a cool, dark place until they are done.

D. *Bran pickles:* This involves pickling in a mixture of bran (rice or wheat) or rice flour, and sea salt. Like *miso* pickles, bran pickles are especially good for weak intestines.

Quickly dry-roast the bran or flour in a skillet over a medium low flame until a nutty fragrance is emitted. Remove from the skillet and allow it to cool.

Firm, root vegetables pickle best but you can also use greens. The vegetables should all be dried before you use them. A few hours under the sun would be great. *Daikon*, carrots and parsnips are best when dried longer (several days), until they bend like rubber.

A ceramic crock or wooden keg again are the best containers to use. Cover the pickles with a cheesecloth and keep the container in a cool, dark place.

There are two ways to make bran pickles.

1) *Bran pickles #1:* Boil some salt and water, let that cool off, place in a crock or keg and thoroughly mix in the roasted bran or flour to form a paste. Take your dried vegetables and totally submerge them into this paste making sure that the vegetables aren't touching each other. Pack this whole thing down until it's firm and solid. Cover with a cheesecloth.

If you slice the vegies into fairly small pieces they will be done in a week or two. You can also leave them whole. Whole root vegetables can take as long as 3–5 months to pickle. Add more salt if you want to pickle for a long time. (Whole leaves take only a couple of weeks.)

As you remove your finished pickles, you can keep adding new vegetables. When you do that, add more bran and salt. Mix the paste once in a while. If kept well, you can use this paste for years as you add and subtract vegetables from it.

Short Time Paste Proportions (1–2 Weeks)

    10–12 cups bran or rice flour
    ⅛–¼ cup sea salt
    3–5 cups water

Longer Time Paste Proportions (Up to 3–5 Months)

> 10–12 cups bran or rice flour
> 1½–2 cups sea salt
> 3–5 cups water

2) *Bran pickles #2:* This method is made by alternating layers of vegetables with layers of the bran and sea salt mixture.

Mix roasted bran with sea salt and cover the bottom of a crock or keg. Then, add a layer of dried vegetables. Add another layer of bran and salt. Keep alternating. The last layer should be bran. Insert a plate or a wooden disc into the crock on top of the mixture, place a heavy weight on top and press the whole thing. The plate or disc should fit inside the container. It should be loose fitting but cover the contents as much as possible. A clean stone or a jar filled with water can be used as a weight. Cover with a cheesecloth and put in a cool, dark place. When water begins to rise, lighten the weight. When pickles are done, rinse off the bran, slice and eat.

Just as in *Bran pickles #1*, you can either slice the vegies into fairly small pieces or leave them whole. As before, whole pieces take a much longer time to pickle and require more salt.

● *Short Time Proportions (1–2 Weeks)*

> 10–12 cups bran or rice flour
> ⅛–¼ cup sea salt

● *Longer Time Proportions (3–5 Months)*

> 1½–2 cups sea salt

Chinese Cabbage Bran Pickles

> 2 heads of Chinese cabbage
> Bran & salt using shorter time proportions

Fig. 27 Chinese cabbage

Separate the individual leaves from the body of the cabbage. Wash, then dry the leaves for two days, preferably under the sun. Make alternating layers of cabbage with sea salt (the bottom and top layers should be salt) and place a plate and heavy weight on top. Water should rise to the level of the plate in 10 hours. If not, add more weight and/or a little more salt. When the water has risen, drain it out thoroughly. Then relayer the cabbage alternating it with the bran. (The bottom and top layers should be bran.) Replace the weight. It should be ready in a week. When done, wash out the bran, slice and serve. (The reason for draining out the water first is to produce a less salty and more sweet tasting pickle. Also, the Chinese cabbage is a pretty watery vegetable. Other vegetables can be layered in one step, using the bran the first time around, as mentioned before this recipe.)

11. Beans and Bean products ▬▬▬

Most helpful dishes include:

For Both Disorders:

Azuki with squash (or other sweet vegetables) and *kombu*

For Diabetes:

Dried *tofu* with sea or land vegetables

For Hypoglycemia:

Fresh *tofu* or *tempeh* with vegetables or *arame*

Beans are high in protein and are a delicious addition to your diet. It is important not to overeat beans, to chew them very well, and to cook them thoroughly, otherwise you can have gas, intestinal problems and a sluggish condition. They should always be a side dish, not compromising more than 15% of the meal. As they make a heavier dish, beans are more appropriate for supper, somewhat less often for lunch and generally not for breakfast.

Azuki beans, chickpeas, lentils and black soybeans are the most yang beans and the best ones to use on a regular basis. Use these beans and/or bean products such as *tofu* and *tempeh* about three to six times a week (but in small quantities) when healing. Other beans such as pintos, kidneys, black beans and red lentils can be eaten occasionally, about once a week or less during the healing process or may be avoided altogether for several months. Soybeans (which are full of protein) need particular attention so that they are cooked thoroughly. They are delicious in combination with vegetables. They can also be eaten in the form of *tofu*, *tempeh*, *natto*, *miso* and *tamari* soy sauce.

Store beans in an airtight container, like a glass jar, in a cool dry place.

When washing beans, first spread them out a little at a time and take out any stones or anything else that may be mixed in. Then place the beans in a bowl and submerge them in water and stir. Rinse off any dust that may rise to the surface. Repeat this about 3 times or until the water becomes clear. As you lift the beans out of the water into a strainer or colander to drain, leave out any heavy dust or residue that may remain in the bottom of the bowl.

Except for red and green lentils, beans may be soaked for a few hours or overnight prior to cooking. This softens them and helps to cook them quicker. *Azuki* beans need only a few hours of soaking and from time to time you may cook them without it, particularly when trying to strengthen an overly yin condition. Soaking is preferred for pinto and kidney beans for more digestibility. Chickpeas and soybeans need it no matter what, as they are so tough. Use the soaking water when cooking.

Salt is to be added towards the end of the cooking process after the beans have already softened, otherwise they will remain hard for a long time. Placing a piece of *kombu* on the bottom of the pot also helps to soften them as well as adding more minerals and flavor. There are three main ways to cook beans.

1. *Boiling:* This is the method I prefer the most as it cooks the beans gently, slowly, thoroughly and they turn out really delicious and much sweeter.

Soak the beans for a few hours or overnight (not necessary for lentils and split peas). Place an optional piece of *kombu* on the bottom, then your choice of optional vegetables and finally the beans on top. Add just enough water to cover the beans a little bit. Place a drop top inside the pot so that it sits directly over the beans. This top should be loose fitting to let steam escape on the sides but large enough to cover the inside as much as possible.

As the beans expand, slowly and gently pour more *cold* water down the sides of the pot from time to time, always enough to just cover them. The sudden cold water helps the beans soften more quickly. Bring this to a boil over a medium flame.

Then, turn the flame to medium low and let it simmer for 45 minutes to an hour or so, continuing to add cold water once in a while. Watch closely to see when more water is needed to prevent burning. Don't stir or mix at all, letting the cooking go on undisturbed. This makes for a tastier dish.

When the beans are 70% done, add salt and/or *miso* or *tamari* soy sauce, remove the drop top, and simmer for another 10–20 minutes or so until the beans are completely soft, boiling away any excess liquid.

Black Soybeans

2 cups black soybeans soaked overnight with ¼ tsp. of sea salt
½ cup onions, diced
¼ cup parsnips, diced
¼ cup lotus root, diced
1 strip *kombu*, 3″–6″ long
5–6 cups spring water added little by little
½ tsp. sea salt
Tamari soy sauce to taste

Layer the ingredients in this order: first the *kombu*, then onions, parsnips, lotus root and finally the black soybeans. Follow the above directions. Serves 6–8.

2. *Pressure-cooking:* This is the best method for chickpeas as they are extremely hard and tough. *Azuki*, pinto and kidney beans can also be pressure-cooked.

Red and green lentils, split peas and black and white soybeans may clog the pressure gauge of the pressure cooker and cause a possible explosion, so it is best to boil them. In the case of the lentils and split peas it doesn't matter much as they soften very quickly anyway. With soybeans, there are three things you can do to make them safer for pressure-cooking.

A. Boil the (presoaked) soybeans and skim off all the foam that rises to the top. When no more foam appears (maybe in a half hour), place them in a pressure-cooker and cook till done.

B. Dry-roast the soybeans before pressure-cooking them. Combining black soybeans with rice or another grain in addition to the roasting, helps even further.

C. Soak black soybeans for several hours or overnight with ⅛ tsp. of sea salt for every cup of beans. This helps to prevent the skins from coming off and clogging the gauge.

Azuki Beans, Squash and *Kombu*
(Gives vitality, strengthens spleen, pancreas, stomach, and digestion.)

1 cup *azuki* beans
2 cups buttercup or Hokkaido squash
1 piece *kombu* 3″–6″ long
3–4 cups spring water
½–1 tsp. sea salt
Optional: miso or *tamari* soy sauce to taste

Fig. 28 *Azuki* beans

Place *kombu* in a pot. Then, cut the squash into big chunks and place them inside followed by the beans and water. Pressure-cook for 45–50 minutes after the pressure has come up, placing a heat deflector underneath and lowering the flame. Then turn off the flame, bring the pressure down, place the beans back on the stove uncovered, add salt and *tamari* or *miso* to taste and simmer for another 5–10 minutes or until any excess water has been boiled away. When squash is not in season, you may use carrots, turnips, rutabagas, parsnips or onions. Also, other beans may be substituted for the *azuki*. Serves 6.

3. *Baking:*   This is delicious in the winter as it is very hearty and it is good for diabetics. However hypoglycemic persons should avoid baked beans initially for several months.

This method takes the longest time to prepare but the results are well worth the wait. Pintos, kidneys and soybeans yield well to baking.

To prepare, first place the presoaked beans in a pot on top of the stove, adding 4–5 cups of water for every cup of beans. Bring this to a boil, and boil for 15–20 minutes to loosen the bean skins.

Then, pour the beans and liquid into a baking pot. (You can place an optional piece of *kombu* underneath.) Cover, place in the oven and bake at 350° F., adding more water from time to time as needed. They may be done in about 3–4 hours depending on the beans you use.

You may add some vegetables halfway through. The salt and/or *tamari* or *miso* should be added after the beans have become soft and creamy. After adding the salt, you can take the cover off and let the beans brown a bit. Then remove from the stove and serve.

Azuki Beans and Chestnuts

> 2 cups soaked *azuki* beans
> 1 cup dried, soaked chestnuts
> 2 pinches sea salt
> 8 cups spring water
> 1 piece *kombu* 3″–6″ long

Bake following the above directions.

Other bean variations (pressure-cooking or boiling preferable:)

1) *Azuki* with carrots and onions
2) *Azuki* with chestnuts
3) *Azuki* with parsnips
4) *Azuki* with raisins and/or rice syrup

Bean Products: ──────────────────────

While you are healing, it is best not to over consume bean products. Have a small amount 2–3 times a week.

1. *Tofu* or soybean curd comes in two forms, fresh and dried. The fresh *tofu* available in Oriental shops is usually prepared using a modern, chemicalized curdling agent and it is best to buy natural *tofu* curdled with *nigari* (which comes from sea salt). This is available in natural food stores. Dried *tofu* is more strengthening and can be used regularly by anyone. Fresh *tofu* is more yin and should be cooked, especially with some sea vegetables, for persons who are recovering from allergies.

a)   *Fresh tofu:*   When you buy fresh *tofu*, open the package and store the *tofu* in the refrigerator submerged in fresh water (throw out the water it came in). Before you cook with it, very quickly rinse it under the tap.

Tofu cooks very quickly and can be boiled, steamed, baked or broiled, sautéed or pan-fried. It's actually done as soon as it's heated up. It can be prepared in many ways.

When boiling *tofu*, cut it into cubes, put it into boiling water and when it rises to the top it is finished. Add it to soup towards the end of preparation. For *miso* soup, put in the *tofu* just before you add the *miso*.

To steam *tofu*, cut it into smaller cubes and steam until it becomes hot.

When sautéing with *tofu*, you don't need to add any extra water as a lot of it will come out of the *tofu*. You can press out the excess liquid. To do this, place the whole cube onto a wooden cutting board and prop the board up on one end. Put another cutting board, a heavy plate or a weight on top of the *tofu* and let it drain for one hour.

When pan-frying, baking or broiling, cut the *tofu* into slabs, heat a thin layer of oil or water in a skillet or baking/broiling sheet, add the *tofu* and cook the slices till they brown and/or become hot. This only takes a few minutes so be careful not to burn them. Before or after cooking you may spread, dip or marinate each slice in one of several sauces or dips including: 1) grated ginger and *tamari* soy sauce, 2) dry-roasted sesame seeds with *tamari* soy sauce, 3) diluted *miso* and chopped onions or scallions.

Boiled *Tofu*, Chinese Cabbage and Carrots

   1 cube of *tofu*
   3–5 Chinese cabbage leaves cut into 1″ slices
   1 carrot cut into very thin slices
   2–3 cups spring water
   1 piece *kombu* 3″–6″ long
   1 Tbsp. *tamari* soy sauce
   2–3 chopped scallions
   1 tsp. grated ginger

Make a *kombu* stock by boiling, then simmering the *kombu* and water for 2–3 minutes. Place the carrots, Chinese cabbage and *tofu* into separate sections of the pot and boil them for a few minutes until they are done. Make a dip by taking 1 tablespoon of the stock and mixing in the *tamari*, scallions and ginger. Serves 2–3.

Tofu Pickle

(An unusual but absolutely delicious dish, it is very similar to cheese.)

1 cube of firm *tofu*
Enough *miso* to coat it completely

Totally coat the *tofu* on all sides with ¼″ layer of *miso* and let it sit. One day later, scrape the *miso* off, slice and serve.

b) *Dried tofu:*   You can buy dried *tofu*. They look like thin, lightly yellow, rectangular wafers. To cook with it, first soak it in water until it softens. Then cut it up into any desired size or leave it whole. This can then be combined with vegetables and treated like one of them. It should be boiled at least 15 minutes. You can also pressure-cook it and add it to soups and stews. Below is a recipe example.

Dried *Tofu, Daikon* and Lotus Root Stew

8 pieces of dried *tofu*, soaked
1 *daikon* cut into 1″ rounds
1 lotus root cut into ¼″–½″ rounds
1 strip *kombu*, 4″–6″
Water to cover ingredients halfway to level
1 pinch sea salt
***Tamari* soy sauce or puréed *miso* to taste**

Layer *kombu, tofu, daikon* and lotus root into a pressure-cooker. Add salt and enough water to cover the ingredients halfway to level. Bring to pressure, then turn the flame to low and simmer for 15 minutes. Uncover, add *tamari* or *miso* to taste, boil away any excess liquid, remove and serve. Serves 4.

3. *Tempeh:*   This is a fermented soy product used in Indonesia and now available in many natural food stores. It's energizing and full of protein. Store it in the refrigerator.

You can cook *tempeh* anywhere from a few minutes to 30 minutes or more. The longer that you cook it the more easily digestible and smoother tasting it becomes.

In boiling, steaming, pressure-cooking, baking and sautéing with vegetables, if the *tempeh* is pan- or deep-fried beforehand it makes the dish extra delicious. It can be deep-fried without any batter or covering. Unlike fresh *tofu*, add it to your dishes in the beginning of the cooking preparation.

Pressure-Cooked *Tempeh* and Vegetables

  1 *tempeh* cut into large chunks
  3 onions quartered
  2 large parsnips cut into triangular wedges
  ½ head cabbage, cut into 2″ squares
  1 burdock cut into 1″ rounds
  ¼ cup of sauerkraut
  3 pinches sea salt

Place all the ingredients into a pressure-cooker and pressure-cook for 15–20 minutes. (The *tempeh* can be deep-fried beforehand.)

4. *Natto:*   This is an odd stringy, fermented soybean preparation. To some individuals at the first encounter, it is also unpleasant smelling. But once a taste is acquired for *natto*, many people can't get enough of it.

This is not an absolutely necessary food such as rice, sea vegetables, greens, root vegetables, *miso*, and so on, so have it only if you want some. It is protein-rich like all the other soy products and good for vitality as well as being very easy to assimilate. You can find this in natural or Oriental food stores.

It usually comes frozen, so you have to thaw it out by leaving it for a day in the refrigerator compartment (out of the freezer) or a few hours in room temperature. Otherwise, store it in the freezer until the day you want to eat it.

Stir in one or more of the following ingredients: 1) grated *daikon*, 2) grated ginger, 3) chopped scallions or 4) diced raw onions with the addition of either 1) *tamari* soy sauce, 2) *umeboshi* paste or 3) sauerkraut. Pieces of *nori* may also be mixed in. These combinations may be eaten on top of your rice or other grains as a condiment or in *miso* soup.

12. Sea Vegetables ━━━━━━━━━━

Sea vegetables are a very important and integral part of the macrobiotic diet. They help purify and strengthen the bloodstream and strengthen the intestines, digestive system, liver, pancreas, sexual organs, and mental clarity and awareness. They also help promote beautiful skin and hair. They can be consumed everyday in some form no matter what your condition. They supply calcium, iron, protein, iodine, and vitamins A, B₁₂, and C as well as various other minerals.

Many people used to (and some still do) cringe at the thought of eating sea vegetables and considered it an esoteric Oriental food. However, they have been consumed traditionally by people all over the world including the Celtics, Vikings, Russians, coastal Africans, Mediterranean peoples, North and South American Indians, native Australians, and the early New England settlers (dulse and *kombu* in their case) as well as in the Far East. Some varieties may take a while to acquire a taste for but it is well worth the effort for all the countless benefits that they bestow.

Sea vegetables are purchased dried (from natural food stores) and can therefore last many years until you use them. They are also easily stored. Any shady, dry place will do.

There are several varieties that are now available. *Kombu* is more tough and may take several hours, unless pressure-cooked, to completely soften. Dulse, on the other hand, can be eaten raw or like *nori*, just toasted for a second.

Wash sea vegetables very quickly to retain as much of their nutrients as possible. Submerge *hijiki, wakame* and *arame* in water, rinse off any dust that floats to the top and lift them out of the water, leaving any sand or stones that sit at the bottom. (*Arame* will probably be pretty clean already as it has been shredded.)

To clean *kombu*, brush off any dirt or dust with a dry or wet towel. Leave the white colored substance (which consist of salt and complex sugars) on the surface of the *kombu* as they contribute to its flavor and value. Dulse doesn't need to be washed in water but check it very carefully for hidden shells, stones, and tiny fish. *Nori* and agar-agar shouldn't be washed.

1. *Arame and hijiki:* *Arame* comes shredded and has a very delicious but mild flavor. *Hijiki* is naturally stringy and looks like a thicker, darker *arame*. It also has a richer taste. *Hijiki* should be soaked for 3–5 minutes beforehand until it expands a bit. Remember that it finally become 3–5 times larger so be careful not to use more than

you need. It isn't necessary to soak *arame*, just *quickly* rinse it once in cold water.

Fig. 29   Dried *arame*   Fig. 30   Dried *hijiki*

Arame and *hijiki* are cooked the same way, though *hijiki* takes a longer time, and one can be substituted for the other. They combine really well with root vegetables or with *seitan, tofu, tempeh,* and fresh corn as well as other ingredients. They are generally sautéed or just simmered with a small amount of water. For diabetes, it is nice occasionally to sauté the vegetables first for a while before adding the sea vegetables.

Arame (or *Hijiki*), Parsnips, Onions, Dried *Tofu*

1 cup soaked *arame* or *hijiki*
1 parsnip cut into thin matchsticks
2 onions cut into thin half-moons
3 dried *tofu*, soaked and cut into several strips
½ Tbsp. dark sesame oil or water
Soaking waters
1–2 Tbsps. *tamari* soy sauce

Soak *arame* (or *hijiki*) until you can slice it easily. Put the *arame* onto a cutting board and cut through it, with the slices being 3″ apart from each other. Then cut some more 3″ slices at right angles to the previous ones.

Place and heat up the oil or water in a skillet. Sauté the onions until they become translucent and remove them. Then layer first the sea vegetable, then the *tofu*, parsnips and finally the onions and add water until it is level with the vegetables. Cover and let this simmer over a medium low flame until everything is soft. Then uncover, add the *tamari*, and simmer another 5–10 minutes or more, boiling away any remaining water. Serves 4–5.

2. *Kombu:* This comes in thick, flat strips which may be anywhere from 3″–18″ long. There are recipes throughout this cookbook using *kombu* as it enhances the flavor of grains, beans and vegetable dishes, helping them to soften and/or effectively combining and synthesizing all the

ingredients into a whole. It also makes an excellent soup stock. (See *Soup* chapter.) In all of those cases, the *kombu* is more like an accessory but you can also use it as a vegetable in its own right. It has a pretty tough texture, so a pressure-cooker really comes in handy though you can also boil it for a while.

Before you can slice it, you need to soak it. It doubles in size when you do. Soak only until it is soft enough to cut. Otherwise, it becomes very slippery and slicing will become difficult.

Fig. 31   Dried *kombu*

Boiled *Kombu*, Onions, Burdock and Turnips

 12″ strip *kombu*, sliced into 1″ squares
 5 onions, quartered
 3 turnips, quartered
 1 burdock cut into 1″ slices
 Soaking water
 1 Tbsp. *tamari* soy sauce

Clean, soak and slice *kombu* and place in the bottom of a pot. Layer onions, turnips and burdock on top. Add enough of the soaking water to half cover the vegetables. Cover, bring this to a boil, turn flame to low, and simmer for 30–45 minutes or until everything is soft. Uncover, add soy sauce and cook another 10 minutes, boiling away excess water. Serves 6.

114

Lotus Root and *Kombu*

1 cup lotus root, sliced into ½ " rounds
6" strip *kombu*, soaked & sliced into 1" squares
Soaking water
A few drops of *tamari* soy sauce

Soak the *kombu* until it's soft enough to slice. Then cut it into 1"
squares. Place it into the bottom of a pressure-cooker and add the
lotus root rounds on top. Add water to be level with the top of the
vegetables. Bring this to pressure and simmer for 15–20 minutes.
Then release the pressure, uncover, add *tamari* to taste and boil away
the excess liquid. (You may also use lotus seeds. Soak them overnight with the *kombu* before cooking them.) Serves 4–5.

3. *Wakame:* This is a thin, leafy type of sea vegetable and cooks quickly.
You can use it in any recipe that calls for *kombu*. As is *kombu*, it is
excellent in grain, bean, vegetable dishes and soups.

Fig. 32 Dried *wakame*

Fig. 33 Soaked *wakame*

Wakame should also be soaked before you can slice it. If the soaking water is a bit salty, you can save it for soups, grains or bean dishes, where it will be more diluted. Or if you want to use some of the flavor that went into the liquid for your *wakame* dish, combine a portion of it with fresh water.

The vein portion takes a longer time to cook so slice that part fairly thinly so that it will be finished when the softer leafy sections (which should be sliced into larger pieces) are.

(Look under *Vegetables*, *Soups* and *Condiments* for more *wakame* recipes.)

Wakame, Broccoli and Onions

2 cups washed, soaked & sliced *wakame*
6 broccoli flowers
1 onion sliced into thin half-moons
Spring water
A handful of dry-roasted sesame seeds
Tamari soy sauce

Slice the vein portion of the *wakame* into smaller pieces than the soft leaf part. Bring water to a boil and boil the broccoli flowers until they turn a bright green. Remove them and drain them in a colander. Boil onions until they become translucent, remove and drain them. Blanch the *wakame* in the boiling water. Remove and drain. Place the three vegetables onto a serving dish, arranging them attractively. Add a few drops of *tamari* to some sesame seeds and sprinkle them on top of the vegetables. Serves about 6.

4. *Nori:* This comes in thin, flat, paper-like sheets. No washing, soaking and cooking is required except to lightly toast it over an open flame for a few seconds. In Japan it is used to garnish noodles, grains, and vegetables as well as acting as wrapping for *sushi* and rice balls among other things.

After toasting the sheets, you can leave them whole (as you would when you make *sushi* rolls) or cut them up with your fingers or scissors into any size pieces that you desire. Very small pieces or slivers make a good decorative garnish on top of noodles, grains, vegetables, and so on. One eighth of a sheet is a nice size for covering and picking up small pieces of grains or vegetables. Two pieces (a quarter of a sheet each) are used to wrap a rice ball.

Norimaki (*Sushi*)
(They are handy as appetizers, snacks and for traveling and have a very decorative appearance.)

1½ cups cooked short-grain (sticks best) brown rice
1 sheet *nori*
1 carrot cut into several lengthwise strips
2–3 uncut (except for the roots) scallions
1″ boiling water in a pot
¼–½ tsp. *umeboshi* paste
1 pinch sea salt

Add a pinch of salt (for brighter vegetable colors) to the pot of boiling water and boil the carrot strips until they are soft. Take the strips out and let them drain. Then, boil the scallions (cut off the roots) for just a second or before they loose the bright green color, take them out and let them drain as well.

Meanwhile, toast a sheet of *nori* by passing it several times over an open flame (on the dull side only for easier rolling) until it's green but not so much that it is overly crisp and crinkly.

Place a *sushi* mat onto a cutting board and the sheet of *nori* on top of it. The halfway fold of the *nori* should be horizontal from you. Wet your hands and evenly press ¼″ layer of rice onto the *nori*, leaving ½″–¾″ of the top edge (the side away from you) and ¼″ of the bottom edge uncovered. Then, make a horizontal indentation in the rice 1″ up from the bottom of the *nori* and spread the *umeboshi* paste inside the length of it. Then press 1–3 carrot strips and the scallions (again horizontally) on top of the paste.

Next, slowly roll the mat and it's contents upwards, pressing firmly upon the rice and other ingredients. Try to tuck the vegetables underneath as you keep rolling. Wet the top edge of the uncovered *nori* (to help in sealing) and complete the roll.

Wash and dry your hands. Place the roll with the sealed edge underneath, wet a vegetable knife (to prevent the rice from sticking to it for smooth, easy cutting), and slowly, carefully but firmly cut the roll into 1″ slices. Place the slices onto a plate with the inside turned upwards to show it's beautiful design, decorate and serve. Serves 5 pieces.

5. *Dulse:* This can be added raw or slightly toasted to soups, salads, and vegetable, grain and bean dishes at the very end of preparation for extra flavor. It can also be lightly toasted by itself, crumbled and used as a condiment.

6. *Agar-agar:* This is used as a jelling agent for *kantens* and *aspics*. You can purchase it in the form of bars or powder with the instructions enclosed. (See *Desserts* chapter for *kanten* recipes.)

13. Seasonings, Condiments, Sauces and Dressings ━━━━━━━━

Besides your foods and cooking methods, seasonings and condiments play a vital part in the balancing of a meal. As with any other aspect of preparing foods, care must be taken to have enough variety. The chart below is a listing of some of the condiments mentioned in this book. They are categorized into the five tastes and making sure that you use something from each column insures a well rounded meal. Some items fit into more than one category. (Don't over use them, especially the salty items. In most cases, just a light accent is enough.)

SOUR	BITTER	SWEET	PUNGENT	SALTY
Pickles	Gomashio	Miso	Ginger	Miso
Sauerkraut	Tekka	Amazake	Scallions	Gomashio
Umeboshi	Green nori	Applesauce	Onions	Umeboshi
Shiso leaves	Parsley	Rice syrup	Grated daikon	Shiso leaves
Rice vinegar	Dandelion	Barley malt	Watercress	Shio kombu
Lemon	Wakame powder	Mirin		Wakame powder
	Mustard greens	Raisins		Tamari soy sauce
	(pickled)			Tekka

Seasonings: ━━━━━━━━

1. *Sea salt:* Salt is one of the building blocks of life and we cannot survive without it. It is one of the basic ingredients of our blood and gives us vitality, strength, and mental clarity. Learning how to adjust salt intake and finding its balance with oil and water is an important part of mastering the art of cooking.

   Only use white unrefined sea salt. In commercial table salt, much of the valuable trace minerals have been removed. Sugar (dextrose), magnesium and sodium carbonate, and potassium iodide has been added in their place. It depletes important minerals from our body as well as contributing to high blood pressure, heart problems, kidney disorders and illness in general. Grey sea salt is also not recommended as it can cause excessive tightness in the body.

   The amount of salt that we can take depends on our individual condition, our age, our activities and environment. Physically active people, adults, persons with a more vegetarian based history, and persons that live in a more wet, humid and cold climate can take more salt. (Babies shouldn't take salt at all. It should be gradually introduced to them as they grow.) Individuals with a history of heavy meat consumption should carefully limit their intake and may even need to abstain for a short period of time. (These are the persons that benefit from vegetarian, raw food, and salt free diets which help to cleanse their bodies. However, after a while, salt and cooked foods should be reintroduced.)

Too much salt can cause hyperactivity, irritability, kidney problems, thirst and anger among other things. Too little can cause poor circulation, mental lethargy, sleepiness, weakness and so on. (Excess salt can also cause these symptoms at times.)

Your meals shouldn't be overwhelmingly salty. Salt should enhance and draw out the natural flavor and sweetness of your foods, not cover them up. Generally, if you're extremely thirsty or crave fatty, rich foods or strong yin such as sugar, ice cream, and so on when you finish your meal, it is an indication that too large a dose of salty (or hot) condiments and dishes may have been consumed. Salt is very yang and attracts much yin, so too much makes it difficult to eat in a centered manner.

Plain salt is not recommended for use at the table. (An exception may be a small pinch of it on your fresh fruits to draw out their sweetness.) It is too strong and difficult to assimilate in that form. Various condiments which substitute for it—such as sea vegetable powders or a mixture of salt and sesame seeds—are recommended. (See the *Condiments* section in this chapter.)

2. *Miso:* *Miso* is a paste made out of fermented soybeans and sea salt which has been aged for a period of a few months to as long as three years or more. If only a few months old it is light in color and contains less salt. If older, the color becomes a dark brown and more salt is needed to keep it going for that long a time.

The darker, longer time *miso* is best for healing and is the kind that is assumed when using *miso* is recommended. The best *miso* is at least two summers old. There are three basic kinds now available in natural food stores. (Don't buy *miso* from Oriental food shops. It may be made without using a natural fermenting process and also may contain chemicals and sugars.)

A. *Hatcho miso:* This is 100% soybeans and is the darkest, most yang variety. It is especially recommended for the cold winter months.

B. *Mugi miso:* This contains barley, is the sweetest of the three and is appropriate all year round as well as being good for medicinal use.

C. *Genmai (brown rice) or kome (white rice) miso:* This contains rice. It is lighter and is good for the summer though it can also be used year round. Use this less often than the first two.

The short term *miso* comes in red, yellow or white. It is sweet, good for the summer and makes delicious sauces and spreads but doesn't have medicinal value.

Buying bulk *miso* is recommended over the packaged variety, especially when one is trying to heal oneself, as it is more alive. When packing, the *miso* has to be pasteurized, otherwise it will keep fermenting and may burst the package.

Keep the *miso* in a cool, dark place and stir it from time to time. (The short term kind should be refrigerated.) If a white color starts to appear on the surface, mix it into the bulk of the *miso*. This substance is a natural bacterial growth and is not harmful. On the contrary, besides adding more minerals and flavor to the *miso*, it is a reassurance that the *miso* is organic and alive.

3. *Tamari soy sauce and/or shoyu:* This is a liquid by-product of the *miso* making process. It contains fermented soybeans, water, sea salt and sometimes a small amount of wheat. Be very careful to avoid commercial *shoyu* as it is artificially aged and is full of chemicals and coloring. To be on the safe side, purchase soy sauce from natural food stores instead of Oriental ones.

Tamari can be added to just about any kind of dish for extra flavor. There are numerous recipes which use it throughout this book.

Like salt and *miso*, *tamari* should always be cooked into foods, not added afterwards at the table as this can make you very tight and disrupt your digestion. Also, be careful that you don't take too much.

4. *Umeboshi plum, paste and vinegar and shiso leaf pickle:* *Umeboshi* plums have very strong medicinal value. They purify the bloodstream, detoxify poisons, stimulate appetite, and at times can help to relieve stomachaches, nausea and air sickness. (Take them along whenever you travel.) When someone isn't feeling well, we separate the meat of the plums from the pit, grind it into a paste with a *suribachi* or just chop it very finely and add it to a thick *kuzu* drink (see *Special Needs* chapter) or serve with rice cream.

Umeboshi plums have been pickled in sea salt and *shiso* leaves (to give it that bright red color) for a year or more. They can be added to just about any dish and may be used as a substitute for salt, *tamari* or *miso*. One plum is a delicious condiment with a bowl of rice or other grains. (See *Grains and Grain Products* chapter for a *Rice ball* recipe.)

Recently, *umeboshi* paste and vinegar (leftover juice from making these pickles) have become available. They are very handy to cook with and can be added to your dishes. However, they don't have the strong healing qualities of the plum. Therefore when making *Special Needs* recipes or when trying to relieve a stomachache (for instance) use the whole plum.

Pickled *shiso* leaves are also available by themselves. They can be sliced and added to your dishes in addition to or as a substitute for salt. They are very valuable when dried or baked and ground into a powder for use as a condiment. In this form, they are helpful for neutralizing strong chemicals in your system.

5. *Oil:* Vegetable oils, which are full of polyunsaturated fatty acids, are needed to build new cells and tissues, to keep warm, for vitamins A and E, to maintain proper metabolism and to lubricate skin and hair among other things. However, much of what you need is already found in grains, beans and seeds so the intake of extra oil can be kept to a minimum, especially during the initial few months of healing. A healthy person can have a small amount of extra oil nearly everyday in a side dish of sautéed vegetables or in a sauce or dressing. Even then, one or two tablespoons are adequate to sauté enough vegetables and grains for a whole family. Also, deep-fried foods shouldn't be consumed more than once a week.

Choose unrefined and cold-pressed oils (meaning that the seeds have been pressed below the boiling point and filtered). This has all the vitamins and nutrients intact, is rich in color, retains the flavor and taste of the original seeds, and is somewhat cloudy in appearance. Please avoid refined oils or oils that have been processed at a high temperature.

Animal oils and fats should be totally avoided as they contain high levels of cholesterol which causes hardening of the arteries and heart disease among other things.

To digest more oily foods such as fried rice, accompany them with grated ginger or grated, raw *daikon* or plenty of chopped raw scallions.

Keep your oils in a tightly sealed container in a cool, dark place or in the refrigerator.

Sesame oil, especially the dark variety made from roasted seeds, is the most healthy one to use as it is easiest to digest and more yang than other varieties. Pumpkin seed oil is an occasional variation, also more yang than other oils.

Corn oil (a lighter oil for pastries or pie crusts), safflower, sunflower and olive oil may all be used occasionally once you are in sound health; it is best to avoid them for now.

6. *Brown Rice Vinegar:* This is to be used occasionally. It is delicious in *sushi*, dressings, grain salads and pickles.

7. *Mirin:* This is a cooking wine made from sweet rice. It is delicous in sweet and sour sauces as well as in beans, vegetables, noodle broths, dressings and marinades. Use this occasionally; it may be avoided initially for several months.

8. *Ginger:* Ginger is a hot, pungent and very delicious root which stimulates the appetite, and activates circulation.

   A small amount of grated ginger spices up your grains, vegetables and noodles. You can extract the juice by squeezing the grated ginger. (The juice is stronger.) Ginger is taken raw or added at the very end of preparations.

9. *Rice syrup and barley malt:* These are the most healthy sweeteners that you can use. They are the honeys of their respective grains and are delicious in desserts or cooked in with *azuki* or black soybeans.

Condiments

Condiments, though we use them very sparingly, are an indispensable part of macrobiotic eating. They add one or more of the following to a meal: color, extra variety and flavor, extra vitamins and minerals, appetite stimulation, balance, zest, and in some cases, medicinal value.

A small amount of various condiments may be used everyday to accompany your grains. They allow individuals to adjust their intake of salt, minerals or oils to fit their own needs. They are easy to overuse so watch out for this, especially when dealing with the more saltier varieties such as *gomashio* or *tekka*.

Gomashio
(The most commonly used condiment in the macrobiotic diet. It is a perfect balance of salt and oil.)

14–16 Tbsps. black or white sesame seeds
1 Tbsp. sea salt

Dry-roast sea salt in a skillet until it becomes shiny. (Roasting releases moisture in the salt and this helps to make a fluffier *goma-shio*.) Place it into a *suribachi*, take the pestle and gently grind it until it becomes a fine powder.

Wash and rinse the sesame seeds and drain them in a fine wire mesh strainer. Place them (they should still be wet) in a skillet and dry-roast them until they pop, emit a nutty fragrance and can be crushed very easily between the thumb and index fingers. Be careful that you don't burn them.

Place the seeds into the *suribachi* with the salt and grind them together until the seeds are half crushed and are all coated with salt. Make gentle circular motions using the grooves on the sides of the *suribachi*. When the *gomashio* cools off, place it into an airtight glass or ceramic container. (If it is still warm, moisture will collect inside the container and cause easy spoilage.) Sprinkle this over your grains and vegetables.

Sesame seeds are high in calcium, protein, iron, phosphorous, vitamin A and niacin. For variety, add sea vegetable powder or *shiso* leaf powder instead of salt. (See *Wakame Powder* and *Shiso Leaf Powder* recipes below.)

Shio Kombu

8 long strips (about 12″) *kombu*
Enough liquid to cover (50% water and 50% *tamari* soy sauce)

Cut the *kombu* into 1″ squares with scissors and soak them in water/*tamari* soy sauce for 1–2 days. Place them into an uncovered pot, add enough water/*tamari* soy sauce to cover, bring to a boil, immediately turn the flame to low, place a heat deflector underneath and slowly simmer for a couple of hours until most of the liquid has evaporated. Since this is very strong, have only one or two pieces at every meal.

Nori Condiment

10 sheets of *nori* broken or cut into small pieces
1 cup spring water
½ Tbsp. *tamari* soy sauce

Bring all the ingredients to a boil in a small covered pot, turn the flame to low and slowly simmer for about 20–30 minutes or until most of the liquid has boiled away, leaving a paste of *nori*.

Wakame/Rice Vinegar Condiment

1 cup *wakame* soaked and sliced
2 Tbsps. brown rice vinegar
2 Tbsps. soaking or fresh water
2 Tbsps. *tamari* soy sauce

Cook as in the *nori* condiment.

Wakame Powder

Roast some *wakame* in the oven at 350° F. for 10–15 minutes or until it is crisp but not burnt. Grind and crush it into a fine powder in a *suribachi*. Dulse and *kombu* powder can also be made this way. This may be ground with sesame seeds; in this case, use a proportion of 4–8:1.

Shiso Leaf Powder

1 cup of *shiso* leaves chopped very finely. Dry-roast *shiso* in a skillet or in the oven at 350° F. until it dries out. Then grind it into a powder. This can be combined with seeds, sea vegetable powder or both.

Sauces and Dressings:

It is generally best to use sauces and dressings sparingly. Properly prepared, most good macrobiotic dishes are beauful and delicious enough to stand on their own. However, it is a nice addition at times, particularly with more bland or lighter dishes and they can add extra dynamics, like condiments, without covering up the taste and other qualities of the dish they accompany.

Kuzu Sauce

> 1–1½ cups soup or vegetable stock
> 1 Tbsp. *kuzu* dissolved in a small amount of water
> *Tamari* soy sauce to taste
> *Optional:* 2–3 pinches grated ginger

Bring dissolved *kuzu* and soup stock to a boil, lower the flame, simmer and stir until the *kuzu* becomes transparent. Add the *tamari* and ginger and place this over grains or vegetables.

Fig. 34 *Kuzu*

Kuzu Sauce with Vegetables

> ½ carrot cut into thin matchsticks
> 1 onion thinly sliced
> 2 cups water or soup stock
> 2–2½ Tbsps. *kuzu* dissolved in a small amount of water

124

Tamari soy sauce to taste
Optional: A couple pinches of grated ginger

Bring vegetables and soup stock to a boil, turn the flame down and simmer until the vegetables are soft. Add the diluted *kuzu* and stir until it becomes transparent. Add the *tamari* and optional ginger.

Onion Butter

Enough thinly sliced onions to more than fill a pot.
½" water
1–2 pinches sea salt

When slicing the onions, leave out all the tough, undissolvable portions. Fill a pot so full that you have to press the onions to fit them inside. Add salt and water and cover. Very slowly, over a low flame, bring this up to a boil. Then turn the flame down even lower, place a flame deflector underneath and simmer for 6–10 hours until the onions shrink to a golden brown paste.

Garnishes

To garnish your dishes you can use *nori*, scallions, parsley, raw onions, sautéed vegetables, red radishes, boiled greens, lemons, grated vegetables, croutons, sliced fruits, roasted seeds and nuts and so on.

Umeboshi Dressing

2 tsps. *umeboshi* paste
½ cup or a little more water
½ tsp. diced onions

Grind paste, onions and water in a *suribachi* into a purée. You can use this for boiled salads, boiled *tofu* or other milder dishes.

Tofu Dressing

1 cube *tofu*
1 tsp. *umeboshi* paste
1 Tbsp. grated onion
2 tsps. more of water

Purée all the ingredients in a *suribachi*.

Miso Dressing

3 Tbsps. puréed *miso*
1 Tbsp. grated onion
2 Tbsps. brown rice vinegar

6 Tbsps. water
Some chopped scallions

Purée all the ingredients together except the scallion which you mix in last.

Tamari/Ginger/Vinegar Dressing

2 Tbsps. *tamari* soy sauce
$\frac{1}{2}$–1 cup water
$\frac{1}{4}$ tsp. grated ginger
8 Tbsps. brown rice vinegar

Mix all the ingredients together.

Fig. 35   Ginger

For variations:

1) *Miso* and *tamari* are interchangeable.
2) *Umeboshi* is interchangeable with *miso* and *tamari* though it doesn't go well with rice vinegar or lemon.
3) Ginger, onions, parsley, scallions and chives are interchangeable and can be used singularly or in combination. Using more than two at one time can get a bit too complicated.
4) Lemon can be substituted for rice vinegar.
5) Heated sesame oil may be left out or added.

14. Desserts

You can make delicious desserts using squash, sweet grains or *azuki* beans as a base, rather than fruit or flour. The best sweeteners for your health are:

1. *Amazake*, a drink or a pudding made out of fermented sweet rice and a starter called *koji*, also made out of rice. It can be consumed as it is as well as being added to other dessert recipes.
2. Rice syrup.
3. Barley malt syrup.
4. Chestnuts.
5. *Mirin*, a cooking wine made from sweet rice. It is used more in regular cooking than in desserts.
6. Raisins and other dried fruits such as apples, peaches, pears, apricots, currants, and cherries.
7. Fresh seasonal fruits cooked.
8. Apple juice and cider.

Agar-agar and *kuzu* are natural thickeners you can use in place of eggs, gelatin, and the like.

For more extensive recipes on cookies, cakes, muffins and so on, refer to other macrobiotic cookbooks. Since this book deals mainly with the healing process, I didn't include these less healthful types of desserts.

Amazake

(Also sold ready-made in some natural food stores.)

> **4 cups sweet brown rice**
> **¹⁄₂ cup *koji* (sold in some natural food stores)**
> **8 cups water**

Soak the rice overnight and pressure-cook for 30 minutes. When done, place it into a glass bowl and as soon as it becomes cool enough to handle, mix in the *koji*, cover with a towel and put it in a warm place. An oven with just the pilot light on or the radiator will do. Let this ferment for 4–8 hours. Mix it once in a while to help dissolve the *koji*. The fermentation is done when bubbles start to appear on the surface together with a sweet taste. It becomes sweeter and sweeter up to a certain point and then it starts to turn sour. Catch it when it's sweet, place it back into a pot, bring it to a boil, add a pinch of sea salt and turn it off as soon as it starts to bubble.

You can use it as it is or you can blend it in a food mill. For a delicious drink, after you blend it, add a small amount of water and optional grated ginger, bring to a boil and serve. Or you can let it cool off to make a refreshing cold beverage.

To keep the *amazake* for a longer time, simmer it over a low flame with a heat deflector underneath until it becomes a little bit brown.

Basic *Amazake* Pudding

4 cups *amazake* drink
6 Tbsps. *kuzu*, dissolved in a small amount of water
2 pinches sea salt
Optional: **¼ cup raisins**

Place all ingredients into a pot, and bring to a boil while stirring constantly with a wooden spoon to avoid lumping and burning. Then simmer for about 3 minutes, pour into a serving plate, let it set, garnish and serve. If it jelled properly, you can slice it into several squares. Serves 8.

Chestnut Sweet Rice

2 cups sweet rice
½ cup dried chestnuts
3 cups spring water
2 pinches sea salt

Wash the chestnuts (sort out discolored ones) and dry-roast them for about 5 minutes in a skillet over a medium low flame. Stir with a wooden spoon, making sure that they don't burn. Put them in a pressure-cooker with the sweet rice and cook as in the *Basic Brown Rice* recipe. Serves 4–6.

Sweet *Azuki* Beans

1 cup *azuki* beans
1 cup chestnuts
⅛ cup raisins (or ½ cup *ame* rice syrup
5 cups water
½ tsp. sea salt

Soak the *azuki* and chestnut for 6–8 hours or overnight. Place all the ingredients except salt into a pressure-cooker and pressure-cook for 40–45 minutes. Let the pressure come down completely, uncover, add salt, bring to a boil again, turn flame to low, and simmer for another 5–10 minutes. Or you can simmer for a longer time, until all the excess liquid has boiled away. (That would make this really sweet.) Serves 4–6.

Ohagi

- 2 cups sweet rice
- 2 cups chestnuts
- 7 cups spring water
- 4 pinches sea salt
- ½ cup black sesame seeds
- 1 Tbsp. *tamari* soy sauce

Dry-roast the chestnuts and pressure-cook them in 5 cups of water and 2 pinches of sea salt for 45–50 minutes. When done, blend it into a purée with a food mill.

Wash and dry-roast the black sesame seeds until they start to pop and emit a nutty fragrance. Put them into a bowl and pour the *tamari* on them.

Meanwhile, pressure-cook the sweet rice in 3 cups of water and 2 pinches of sea salt for 40–45 minutes. When it's done, vigorously pound the rice with a wooden pestle until the grains are half broken (in 15–20 minutes). Wet your hands and form the rice into small balls.

Coat some of the balls in sesame seeds and *tamari* by rolling them in the seeds. Coat the other ones in the chestnut purée by molding the purée onto them. Place them onto serving plates, creating some kind of attractive decoration with the two different kinds of balls and some garnish. Serves 4.

You can also coat them with either the *Sweet Azuki Beans* dish mentioned above, some dry-roasted, finely chopped walnuts mixed with *tamari* or a squash purée.

Squash Pudding

- 1 buttercup or Hokkaido squash
- 1 cup cooked brown rice
- 2 cups water
- 1 cup barley malt
- ⅛ tsp. sea salt
- 1 Tbsp. *kuzu* diluted in a little water

Bring all the ingredients except the *kuzu* up to pressure in a pressure-cooker, then turn the flame to low and simmer for 15–20 minutes. Turn off the flame, let the pressure come down completely, uncover, add the diluted *kuzu*, and stir constantly until the *kuzu* becomes transparent. Serve hot. Serves 4–6.

Couscous Cake with Pumpkin Seeds and Raisins

- 2 cups couscous
- 1 cup raisins

½ cup dry-roasted pumpkin seeds
¾ cup water or apple juice
1 pinch sea salt

Steam couscous for 5–7 minutes, remove, fluff it up with a fork and add pumpkin seeds to it.

Boil and simmer raisins, water or juice, and salt for 3 minutes. Remove and mix all the ingredients together and press them into a cake pan. Let cool, slice and serve. Serves 6.

Sweet *Kuzu*

1 tsp. *kuzu*
1 Tbsp. rice syrup or barley malt syrup
1 cup water

Dissolve the *kuzu* in 2 teaspoons of water until it becomes a liquid and put it into a pot with 1 cup of water and either rice syrup or barley malt. Stirring constantly with a wooden spoon, bring this to a boil, turn the flame to low, simmer 10–15 minutes and serve hot.

Rice Syrup/Sesame Seed *Kanten*

2 cups water
2 cups *ame* syrup
½ cup sesame seeds
⅛ tsp. sea salt
1 bar agar-agar or 6 Tbsps. agar-agar flakes

Wash, dry-roast and crush the sesame seeds into a fine powder in a *suribachi*. Then stir and boil all the ingredients and simmer for 15 minutes. Wet a mold (so that the *kanten* will be easy to take out when done) and pour all the ingredients into it. Refrigerate for an hour or so until it jells. Serves 8.

Blueberry *Kanten*

2 cups blueberries
4 cups apple juice (or 2 cups juice & 2 cups water)
⅛ tsp. sea salt
1 bar agar-agar or 6 Tbsps. agar-agar flakes
1 Tbsp. *kuzu* diluted in a little water

Bring the juice (or juice and water), salt, agar-agar and *kuzu* to a boil, turn the flame to low, simmer and keep stirring until the *kuzu* becomes transparent and the agar-agar dissolves completely. Then add the blueberries. Place a little coating of water into a mold (so that the *kanten* will be easy to remove later on) and place everything into it and let it sit until it sets. Vary with other fruits. Dried fruits should be added in the beginning of the preparation as they need time to soften. Nuts can also be added. Serves 8.

Applesauce

    8 apples, cored, peeled and sliced
    Water to keep them from burning, about ½ "–1" deep
    2 Tbsps. rice syrup (*optional*)
    2 pinches sea salt
    1 Tbsp. *kuzu* (optional: for a very yin condition)

Bring everything to a boil, then turn the flame down and simmer until the apples become soft. Purée in a food mill and serve. Serves 2–3.

Pie Crust (Regular)

    4 cups whole wheat pastry flour
    1 cup corn oil
    Just enough cold water to hold it together
    1 tsp. sea salt

Mix flour and salt, add the oil while stirring with a fork until little balls and lumps start to form. Gradually add water until you can form a ball of dough as you keep stirring with the fork. This dough should not be sticky and watery. If it is, sprinkle in some more flour.

Separate the dough in two. Take a rolling pin and one of the halves of dough and roll it out flat in between two sheets of wax paper. You can work on top of a cutting board. If the bottom paper slides around too much, wet it's underside slightly. You can also sprinkle some flour or brush a little oil where the paper and dough make contact to prevent them from sticking together. However, if the dough isn't so wet to begin with, this shouldn't be much of a problem. Carefully peel off the paper on top, turn the dough upside down and center it into a pie plate. Then peel off the other side. If you are making an open face pie, first trim away the excess dough that hangs over the edge with a knife. Then with your fork, poke some air holes in the crust to let steam escape (otherwise it will get bubbly) and fasten the outer rim of the crust onto the pie plate by indenting little grooves all around the edge. Use the other half of the dough for another pie. Bake the empty shell for 10 minutes at 375° F. Then take it out, add the filling and bake again until the crust turns a golden brown.

If you are making a pie with a top crust, after inserting the bottom one, add the filling, roll out the other half of the dough and place it on top in the same manner as you did before. Trim away the excess dough. Again, with the fork, poke some air holes in the top crust and seal the upper and lower crusts together by indenting grooves around the outer rim. Then bake.

You can roll out the leftover dough, slice it and bake the pieces as cookies.

Pie Crust (*Mochi*)
(This is a much healthier alternative to regular pie crust but is only practical for open faced pies.)

Cook and pound some sweet rice as in the *Mochi* recipe but then, instead of making the *mochi*, oil a pie plate and press the rice into it and shape a pie crust. Then bake as usual. This doesn't need to be prebaked before adding your filling.

Squash Pie

1 large cubed & peeled buttercup squash
1 cup barley malt
½ tsp. sea salt
¼ cup water
½ cup dry-roasted, chopped walnuts

Pressure-cook (15–20 minutes) the squash with water and salt and purée it in a food mill. Place back into a pot, bring to a boil, add the barley malt, and simmer another 10 minutes. If it is too thick add more water and if too thin, keep simmering until it thickens some more. It should be pretty thick. Place in a prebaked pie shell and sprinkle chopped walnuts on the top. Bake at 350°–365° F. for a half hour or until the crust is golden brown. Chestnuts, fruits and other sweet vegetables may also be used as filling.

15. Fish

Fish should be eaten as fresh as possible, preferably the same day it is caught or at least the same day it is purchased. Choose more slow moving, soft white-meat and yin fish such as sole, flounder, haddock, carp and so on, as opposed to more active, red-meat varieties such as tuna, salmon, swordfish, and the like. Temporarily avoid shellfish such as clams, oysters, mussels, shrimp, lobsters and crabs.

It is best for skin allergic persons to avoid all fish entirely, at least for several months or until symptoms have improved.

Eat two or three times the regular amount of hard leafy greens when including fish in a meal to help balance, it's strong yang energies. Grated *daikon* with a few drops of *tamari* soy sauce and a bit of grated ginger will help neutralize any possible toxic side-effects of the fish. A few drops of lemon is helpful and a slice of lemon is a beautiful garnish as well.

Clear Fish Soup

> 1–2 fillets of sole (or other white-meat fish)
> 1 cup *wakame* soaked & cut into 1″ slices
> 1 bunch watercress, previously boiled for 1 second
> 3 *shiitake* mushrooms, soaked and sliced
> 5–6 cups *kombu* stock (add *shiitake* soaking water)
> *Tamari* soy sauce to taste

Bring *wakame*, *shiitake* and *kombu* stock to a boil, turn the flame down and simmer for a few minutes until the *wakame* and *shiitake* soften. Cut the fish into 1½″–2″ pieces and add them to the soup with *tamari* to taste and simmer for 1–2 minutes or until the fish turns white. Ladle the soup into individual serving bowls and garnish with the watercress. Serves 6–8.

Fish Stew

> 1 lb. cod (or other white-meat fish)
> 12 thin slices lotus root
> 9 ½″ *daikon* rounds, cut in half
> 2 12″ strips *kombu*, soaked and softened
> 6 cups water (including *kombu* soaking water)
> 4–5 tsps. *kuzu*, dissolved in a little bit of water
> *Tamari* soy sauce to taste
> 3 chopped scallions

Cut the *kombu* into 1″ squares and boil in the soaking water until soft. Add the vegetables and the rest of the water and boil and simmer until they are soft. Cut the fish in 2″ slices and add to the soup with the *tamari* and *kuzu*. Stir and simmer 3–5 minutes until the soup thickens a bit. Garnish with chopped scallions and serve. Serves 6–8.

Koi Koku (Carp Soup)

(This very strong soup increases strength and vitality. In Japan it is served to mothers who have just given birth. It is delicious in the winter and medicinal for those who have become very weak.)

   1 small carp (about 2 lbs.)
   Equal volume of thinly shaved burdock
   ½–1 cup *bancha* tea twigs and leaves (already used to make tea)
   Enough liquid to cover, ⅓ *bancha* & ⅔ water
   Grated ginger
   ***Miso* to taste, puréed**
   Clean, 100% cotton cheesecloth

Buy a fresh carp, preferably a live one and ask the fish seller to kill it for you. Also ask him to carefully (so as not to break it) remove the gallbladder and the yellow bitter thyroid bone. Leave the rest of the fish intact.

At home, chop the whole fish (bones, head, fins and all) into 1″ slices.

Make a sack out of the cheesecloth and put the used *bancha* twigs inside like a tea bag. This helps to soften the fish bones.

Place all the ingredients (including the sack of used tea twigs) except the *miso* into a pressure cooker. Pressure-cook for 1 hour. Bring down the pressure, take off the lid, add the ginger and *miso* to taste, simmer for 5 minutes and serve. Garnish with chopped scallions. Serves 6–8.

Baked Schrod

   1 schrod, washed
   3 Tbsps. white *miso*
   2 Tbsps. *mirin*
   3 Tbsps. *kombu* stock
   Grated *daikon*

Place schrod on an oiled baking dish. Make several shallow diagonal slits along the top of it and bake 7–10 minutes.

Meanwhile, purée and mix the *miso*, *kombu* stock and *mirin* in a *suribachi*. Pour this over the baking fish when it is 70% done, bake another 5 minutes and serve with grated *daikon*. Serves 1–2.

Broiled Haddock

2 lb. haddock filet
¼ cup water
¼ cup *tamari* soy sauce
3 Tbsps. *mirin*
1 Tbsp. grated ginger
Several Tbsps. grated *daikon*
A few drop of *tamari* soy sauce
Several parsley sprigs
Several lemon wedges

Mix the water, *tamari*, *mirin* and ginger. Wash the haddock and marinate it in this mixture for 10–15 minutes. Then place the fish on an oiled baking sheet and broil for 4–5 minutes on one side only. Remove, place on a serving platter and garnish with parsley sprigs and lemon wedges. Accompany it with a small dish of grated *daikon* with a few drops of *tamari* added to it. Serves 4.

16. Beverages ━━━━━━━━━━━━━━━

It is best to drink only when we are thirsty. Most of us drink out of habit, whether we want to or not (as we do with food). If you are always thirsty some of the dietary reasons may include:

1) **Overconsumption of salt.**
2) **Overconsumption of animal products.**
3) **Overconsumption of dry, baked and or floury foods.**
4) **Overconsumption of spices**
5) **Overconsumtion of food in general.**
6) **Not chewing enough**
7) **Lack of fresh, light dishes**
8) **Excess of sea vegetables**

Good quality water, such as spring or well water is the best to use. Avoid distilled or highly chemicalized tap water as much as possible.

It is also best to avoid iced or cold drinks (even water) as they can shock and paralyze your digestive system and harden fat accumulations in the body.

The beverages used on a daily basis don't contain caffeine, sugar, carbonation, artificial color, preservatives, stimulants or alcohol (particularly the hard liquor varieties). If you are following a more general Standard Diet you can bend this a bit and have small occasional quantities of more yin, good quality drinks such as green tea, beer, *saké* and mint teas. But on a diabetes or hypoglycemic healing diet, these items are best avoided.

The recipes in the *Special Needs* chapter are to be used only when really necessary and for a short period of time.

Bancha Twig Tea (*Kukicha*)
(For daily use, the brown rice of beverages.)

> **1–2 Tbsps. *bancha* twigs**
> **1½ quarts water**

Twig tea generally comes pre-roasted. If it isn't, dry-roast the whole package of twigs and leaves in a skillet for 3–4 minutes while stirring gently with a wooden spoon. Take out the 1–2 tablespoons that you are going to use and store the rest, after cooling, in an airtight jar until needed.

Add twigs to cold water, bring them to a boil, reduce the flame to low and simmer 10–15 minutes, depending on how light or dark you want it. While serving the tea into individual cups, use a bamboo tea strainer (available in natural or Oriental food stores) to strain out the twigs. A regular metal strainer can be used as an alternative. The twigs may be reused several times until they lose their strength but make it fresh on a regular basis.

Kukicha contains no caffeine, artificial colorings or dyes and is not aromatic. It aids digestion and helps to settle an acidic stomach as it is alkaline in nature. (Most teas are acidic.)

Kukicha or *bancha* is made from the twigs and leaves of an older, matured tea bush, named *ban* in Japanese. (*Cha* is the Japanese word for tea. Hence, saying "*bancha* tea" is really calling it *ban* tea tea.)

The same bush also supplies some green tea which is made from the topmost and youngest, greenest leaves. This tea is delicious but contains much caffeine and is not recommended for regular use. As the bush becomes older, the caffeine content begins to decrease and finally disappears. Harvesting different sections of the plant and at different stages in it's growth produces a variety of teas.

Homemade Grain Teas
(Good for daily or regular use.)

To make grain teas, wash and dry-roast one of the following; rice, millet, oats, barley, wheat, etc., in a dry skillet. Use a wooden spoon to stir. Store what you don't need in an airtight container, after cooling, for later use. Take 2 Tbsps. for 1½–2 quarts of water and boil and simmer as in *bancha* tea.

Mugicha (Roasted Unhulled Barley Tea)
(Good for daily or regular use.)

2 Tbsps. *mugicha* (available in natural food stores)
1½–2 quarts water

Place the *mugicha* in cold water, bring it to a boil, reduce the flame to low and simmer several minutes, the time depending on how strong you want it.

Yannoh/Grain Coffee/Root Coffee
(For more "occasional use")

4 tsp. *yannoh*
4 cups water

Bring *yannoh* and 4 cups of cold water to a boil. Immediately reduce the flame (as it will boil over), and simmer for several minutes.

Yannoh is sold in natural food stores but may be difficult to find. (When buying grain coffee, make sure that it doesn't contain fruits or more yin vegetables such as beets.) You can make your own homemade *yannoh* by washing, separately dry-roasting (till a nutty fragrance is emitted) and grinding.

Yannoh

3 cups brown rice
2½ cups wheat
1½ cups *azuki* beans
2 cups chickpeas
1 cup chicory root

When it's cool, store it in an airtight glass jar. You can experiment and vary different proportions of grains, beans and vegetables (like burdock or dandelion root) with chicory to find a winning combination. One hundred percent dandelion root coffee can be delicious.

Azuki Bean Tea
(For occasionally use, often used medicinally.)

1 cup *azuki* beans
3–4 cups water
1 piece *kombu*

Put *kombu* in the bottom of a pan, then add *azuki* beans and water. Boil, reduce the flame to low and simmer until the water becomes a rich red. This is good for tight kidneys. Have one cup a day for 3 days to help loosen them.

Kombu Tea
(For "occasional use.")

1 strip *kombu*, 6″
2 cups water

Boil the *kombu* and water until only 1 cup of liquid remains.

Mu Tea
(For "occasional use" only.)

1 tea bag of *Mu* tea (sold in natural food stores)
4 cups water

Boil, reduce flame and simmer for 10 minutes. *Mu* tea is made of 9–16 different herbs. The mixture was concocted by my teacher, George Oshawa, the man who first introduced macrobiotic principles to the Western countries.

Umeboshi Tea
(For "occasional use.")

3–4 *umeboshi* plums
1½–2 quarts water
***Optional:* 1 or 2 *shiso* leaves**

Separate the meat of the *umeboshi* from the pits and tear them into several pieces. Add the *umeboshi* meat and pits to the water and bring everything to a boil. Turn the flame to low and simmer for 20–30 minutes. This is delicious when cooled in the summer. It also helps to reduce thirst and replaces minerals lost by excessive sweating.

Leftover Vegetable Juice
("Occasional use")

You can drink the leftover water from boiling or pressure-cooking vegetables. Just make sure that there isn't a lot of concentrated salt in the water.

Vegetable and Fruit Juices
("Occasional use")

The juice of any "regular use" vegetable or seasonal fruit on the *Standard Macroliotic Diet* list may be taken once in a while. In the winter it is preferable to heat juices up, especially the yinner fruit juices. They may be helpful occasionally to help recover from a hypoglycemic episode, especially when heated.

17. Special Needs ▬▬▬▬▬▬▬

You can supplement your meals with some home remedies. For more information about their use, read the companion book (*Macrobiotic Health Education Series*) as well as the chapter on *Dietary Adjustments for Diabetes and Hypoglycemia* in this book.

Internal remedies: ──────────────────────

Agar-agar with *Ame* or Barley Malt
(To relieve constipation.)

    1½ Tbsps. agar-agar flakes
    1 Tbsp. *ame* rice syrup or barley malt
    1 cup spring water
    1 pinch sea salt

Bring all the ingredients to a boil, then turn the flame down and simmer 5–10 minutes. Remove the pot from the stove and take it while it is still warm.

***Daikon* Tea**

    2 Tbsps. grated *daikon*
    A few drops *tamari* soy sauce
    1 teacup hot *bancha* tea

Place *daikon* and *tamari* soy sauce in a drinking cup, fill the cup with hot *bancha* tea, stir and drink.

***Daikon*/Carrot Tea**

    1 Tbsp. grated carrot
    1 Tbsp. grated *daikon*
    A few drops *tamari* soy sauce
    1 teacup hot *bancha* tea

Place the grated carrot and *daikon* and the *tamari* soy sauce in a drinking cup, fill the cup with hot *bancha* tea, stir and drink.

***Kombu* Tea**

    2 cups water
    1 piece *kombu*, 3″–6″

Bring *kombu* and water to a boil, reduce the flame to low, and simmer until only 1 cup of water remains.

Tamari Bancha

A few drops *tamari* soy sauce
1 teacup hot *bancha* tea

Place a few drops of *tamari* soy sauce into a teacup. Pour in hot *bancha* tea, stir and drink.

Ume-Sho-Kuzu
(Strengthens digestion, energizes.)

1 heaping tsp. *kuzu*
1 tsp. *tamari* soy sauce
1 *umeboshi* plum
⅛ tsp. fresh grated ginger
1 cup spring water

Grate the ginger and chop the meat of the *umeboshi* plum and put it aside. Dissolve the *kuzu* in a teaspoons of water until it becomes a liquid and add it to a small pot with 1 cup of water. Bring this to a boil, then turn the flame to low as you stir constantly with a wooden spoon. When the milky white color turns transparent, add the *tamari* soy sauce, *umeboshi* and ginger. Drink this immediately while it's hot.

Shredded *Daikon* Tea

¼ cup shredded dried *daikon*
2 cups water
1 pinch sea salt

Boil the shredded dried *daikon* (available in many natural food stores) in 2 cups of water and the sea salt until only 1 cup remains, and drink.

Lotus Seeds and *Kombu*

½ cup lotus seeds soaked overnight
3″ strip *kombu* soaked & cut into thin matchsticks
A few drops *tamari* soy sauce
Enough water to cover seeds

Bring the lotus seeds, *kombu* and water to a boil, then turn the flame to low and simmer about 30 minutes until the seeds and *kombu* become soft. Then add a few drops of *tamari* soy sauce to taste and simmer another 5 minutes. You can also use fresh or dried lotus root.

External treatments: ───────────────────────────────

Ginger Compress
(Helps circulation, dissolves mucus, cysts, tumors, etc.)

 6 Tbsps. grated ginger
 1 gallon water
 Cheesecloth 6″ by 6″
 Rubber gloves
 3 cotton towels
 Optional: hot plate
 (A person to give the treatment. It's awkward and not relaxing to do
  it yourself.)

Bring a pot of water to a boil and turn the flame off. Meanwhile, make a sack out of cheesecloth, place the grated ginger inside, and tie the open end into a knot to close it. Immediately after turning off the flame and the bubbles have disappeared, squeeze as much ginger liquid as you can out of the sack and into the pan. Then, place the whole bag inside. The point is to put the ginger in as hot a water as possible without boiling it, as that would cancel its effectiveness.

Lay the patient down on a bed or some cushions and let him/her relax. Put on some rubber gloves. Holding both ends of a cotton towel, dip as much of the towel as you can into the water. Wring it out and place it on the affected area of the patient's body. If it's too hot, shake it a bit before placing it on. Ideally it should be as hot as one can stand. Cover this with a dry cotton towel to keep it warm for a longer time. Place another towel in the water and when the first towel has cooled off, wring this one and exchange it with the first. Again, cover with the dry towel. Continue alternating the towels until the area being treated becomes red. You can reheat (but not boil) the water a bit if it becomes too cool.

This treatment, which softens stagnated tumors, mucus deposits, and the like, is sometimes followed by some kind of plaster which helps to draw out the poisons that have been loosened.

Buckwheat Plaster
(Draws out excess fluid from swollen areas.)

 Buckwheat flour
 Enough hot water to form a hard, stiff dough
 5–10% grated ginger
 Clean cotton linen

Precede the plaster with a 5 minute application of ginger compress on the swollen area. Form a dough with the flour, hot water and ginger, and place a ½″ layer on the affected area. Cover and tie it on with a strip of linen. Replace the buckwheat every 4 hours. The swelling should go down after several applications or at the most after 2–3 days.

Lotus Root Plaster
(Draws out excess mucus, especially from the sinuses, lungs and bronchi.)

> **75–85% grated fresh lotus root**
> **10–15% pastry flour**
> **5–10% grated ginger**
> **Cotton linen**

Mix these ingredients and spread them ½″ thick onto a linen cloth. Apply the plaster directly to the skin on the area you are treating. Tie and keep this on for a few hours or overnight and repeat this for a few days. It's helpful to do a ginger compress beforehand.

Daikon Leaves Hip Bath
(For female sexual organ troubles.)

> **4–5 bunches dried _daikon_ leaves**
> **4–5 quarts water**
> **1 handful sea salt**
> **A bathtub of waist level hot water**
> **A towel**

Dry several bunches of fresh _daikon_ tops or greens in the shade until they become dry and brittle. (Use turnip greens if _daikon_ isn't available.)

Boil the dried tops with the handful of salt until the 4–5 quarts of water turns brown. Straining out the leaves, pour the liquid into the bathtub. The water in the tub (make it hot) should come up to waist level. With a towel covering the upper part of your body, sit in the tub until the whole body becomes warm and begins to sweat (about 10 minutes). Do this for as many days as needed. Follow the bath with a _bancha_ tea douche (see below).

Bancha Tea Douche
(For female sex organs.)

> **Enough luke-warm _bancha_ tea for douching**
> **½ tsp. sea salt**
> **Juice from half a lemon or equivalent amount of brown rice vinegar**

Combine all the ingredients and use as a douche after taking the _daikon_ leaves hip bath.

Greens with Bran Plaster
(Helps to reduce discomfort from skin irritation or inflammation.)

50% rice bran
50% finely chopped, raw, green leafy vegetables
A little water to help make a paste
Cotton linen

Crush the hard leafy, chopped greens (such as collards, kale, watercress, etc.) in a *suribachi* until they turn into a pulp. Combine with the bran and some water to make a paste. Apply on the feverish area and remove it when the paste becomes warm or hot.

Greens with *Nori* Plaster
(Also helps to reduce discomfort from skin irritation or inflammation.)

Finely chopped, raw, green leafy vegetables.
A few sheets of *nori*

Crush the greens (such as collards, kale, watercress, etc.) and *nori* in a *suribachi* until they become a pulp and apply this on the feverish area until the paste becomes warm or hot.

Tofu Plaster

1 cake fresh *tofu*
Equivalent amount of finely diced cabbage
Enough whole wheat flour to hold it together, about 10–20% of the plaster
1 tsp. grated ginger

Grind the *tofu* and cabbage into a paste in a *suribachi*. Add the ginger and flour and place this plaster mixture onto a cheesecloth or cotton cloth, forming a sack with the *tofu* inside. Put this onto the forehead or any other affected area using the cheesecloth to tie it in place. When the mixture becomes warm, perhaps every 2–3 hours, exchange it for a fresh application.

Rice Bran Wash

Take two handfuls of bran. Make a sack for it out of a cotton cloth or cheesecloth (several layers thick), put in the bran and tie it tightly. Use this to scrub your body when you take a bath or shower. It can be used several times until it starts to spoil. This is also good for skin rashes.

Glossary

Agar-agar—A white gelatin made from sea vegetable, used for making *kanten*. You can get it in bars or flakes.

Ame—A natural grain honey derived from rice, barley or wheat.

Amazake—A sweet porridge or drink made from fermented sweet rice. You can make this at home or get it in some natural food stores.

Arame—A variety of sea vegetable.

Arepas—Corn cake made from *masa* corn dough.

Arrowroot—A finely ground white flour, used as a thickener, similar to *kuzu* and corn starch.

Azuki beans—Small, red beans. They're good for the kidneys.

Bancha—Tea made from a tea bush which is at least three years old. It helps digestion, and is good for daily use.

Burdock—A long, thin, dark, black root which grows all over the states as well as in other parts of the world. It gives one strength and stamina.

Couscous—A partially refined cracked wheat. It's light and cooks quickly. It is good for summer cooking.

Daikon—A long, thick, white root from the radish family. It is pungent when raw and is sweet when cooked. It is an excellent cleanser and purifier of blood by cutting down on excess fat deposits. Grated raw and with a drop of *tamari* soy sauce, it is a good garnish with oily, greasy foods, making them more digestible.

Dulse—A variety of sea vegetable harvested in Maine, among other places.

Fu—Derived from wheat gluten, you can buy it in natural food stores in either flat, thin sheets or in round donut shapes. When dry it is like a cracker but when cooked it is more like a noodle. A fun food.

Ginger—A hot, pungent, gnarly-looking, flesh colored root. It adds zest to your dishes and also helps circulation whether taken internally or applied externally as in a ginger compress.

Ginger compress—An external treatment made from grated ginger and hot water. It stimulates ciruclation and unblocks stagnation (see *recipe*).

Gomashio—A condiment made from roasted sesame seeds and sea salt.

Hijiki—A black stringy variety of sea vegetable.

Hokkaido squash—A delicous squash, similar to buttercup.

Jinenjo—A very hardy, long, flesh colored, mountain root potato. When grated it becomes a sticky mass and can be eaten with grains or you can slice it and add it to vegetable dishes. It gives one strength.

Kanten—A jello type food made from agar-agar. It makes a great light dessert when made with fruit and fruit juice. It's also used for aspics.

Kasha—Buckwheat groats.

Kinpira—Thinly sliced or shaved, sautéed burdock dish with or without carrots and seasoned with *tamari* soy sauce.

Koji—Rice which has been innoculated with a form of bacteria. It is used as a starter for making *amazake*, *saké*, *miso* and *tamari* soy sauce.

Kombu—A long, smooth, flat, thick variety of sea vegetable used in soup stocks, vegetable, beans, grain dishes and condiments.

Kukicha—Another name for *bancha*.

Kuzu—A starch made from the root of the *kuzu* plant (called *kudzu* in the States) which is used as a thickener in vegetables dishes as well as for medicinal purposes. When you buy it, it looks like little white rocks.

Lotus root—A tubular, flesh colored root from the water lily family. It is hollowed out by several lengthwise airholes. It's good for the respiratory system and helps to unclog the sinuses.

Lotus seeds—Seeds of the above. They look like chickpeas.

Masa—A whole corn dough used as a base for *arepas*, *tortillas*, porridges and so on. You make it at home but some natural food stores have started carrying already made.

Mirin—A sweet wine made from rice and used in cooking.

Miso—A salty paste made from fermented soybeans with or without grains. Many varieties are available (see *Soup* section).

Mochi—Cakes made from pounded sweet rice which are dried and later used in a variety of dishes. It can be made at home or purchased in a natural food store. Make sure to get the brown rice variety instead of the white.

Mugicha—Tea made from roasted barley.

Natto—Stringy, fermented soybeans which when mixed with scallions, *tamari* soy sauce, grated ginger and *daikon*, makes an excellent companion to a bowl of rice. The taste for it has to be acquired for some people. A good source of protein. It can be homemade or store bought.

Nishime—A method of cooking vegetables with a minimal amount of water.

Nori—A variety of sea vegetable which comes compressed into thin paper-like sheets. It can be used as a garnish, a cover for *sushi* and rice balls and also as a condiment.

Norimaki—A type of *sushi* which is made by rolling *nori*, rice and vegetables together into a long roll with a *sushi* mat.

Ohagi—Little balls of cooked, sweet rice which can be covered with seeds, nuts, or *azuki* beans among other things.

Ojiya—A porridge of soft rice, vegetables and *miso* (sea salt or *tamari* soy sauce can substitute for the *miso*).

Sea salt—Salt from the sea, much healtheir than commercial land salt which contains iodine, sugar and chemicals.

Seitan—Wheat gluten which has been boiled (and optionally deep-fried as well) with *tamari* soy sauce, *kombu* and water. It's a good replacement for meat.

Shiitake—A variety of dried mushroom which is helpful in breaking down animal fats within the body. It is used as a soup stock or in vegetable dishes.

Shio kombu—A condiment made from *kombu* and *tamari* soy sauce.

Shiso—Beefsteak plant leaves which are pickled with *umeboshi* plums for added color. It strengthens blood quality and can be used as a condiment.

Soba—Japanese buckwheat noodles.

Somen—An extremely thin variety of Japanese wheat noodles.

Suribachi—A ceramic bowl with grooves and a pestle for grinding and puréeing.

Sushi—Rice formed into little balls and topped with fish or vegetables as well as rolls (*norimaki*) made from *nori*, rice and vegetables.

Sushi mat—Bamboo mat used for making *norimaki sushi*.

Takuan—*Daikon* rice-bran pickles.

Tamari—A name given to naturally made soy sauce to differentiate it from the commercially made, chemicalized ones.

Tekka—A strong condiment made out of burdock, carrots, lotus root, ginger, *miso* and sesame. Available in natural food stores.

Tempeh—Cakes of fermented soybeans, used widely in Indonesia and available in natural food stores. A good source of protein.

Tofu—A white cake made from soybeans and water, also known as bean curd, available fresh or dried.

Udon—Japanese wheat noodles.

Umeboshi—Salty pickled plums. Helps cleanse the blood and aids digestion.

Wakame—A thin, leafy variety of sea vegetable.

Yannoh—Grain beverage sometimes used as a coffee substitute—made from five different grains.

Bibliography

Macrobiotic Health Education Series, Japan Publications.
   a) Kushi, Michio with John D. Mann, *Diabetes and Hypoglycemia*, Tokyo, Japan Publications, 1985
   b) Kushi, Michio with Mark Mead and John D. Mann, *Allergies*, Tokyo, Japan Publications, 1985
Macrobiotic Food and Cooking Series, Japan Publications
Kushi, Aveline with Rosalind Rhodes, *Cooking for Health. Allergies*, Tokyo, Japan Publications, 1985

COOKBOOKS

Aihara, Cornellia, *Macrobiotic Kitchen*, Tokyo, Japan Publications, 1983
Aihara, Cornellia, *The Do of Cooking*, Chico, CA, George Ohsawa Macrobiotic Foundation, 1972
Esko, Edward and Wendy, *Macrobiotic Cooking for Everyone*, Tokyo, Japan Publications, 1980
Esko, Wendy, *Introducing Macrobiotic Cooking*, Tokyo, Japan Publications, 1978
Estella, Mary, *Natural Foods Cookbook: Vegetarian Dairy-free Cuisine*, Tokyo, Japan Publications, 1985
Kushi, Aveline and Oredson, Olivia, *Macrobiotic Cooking for Cancer*, 1984.
Kushi, Aveline, *How to Cook with Miso*, Tokyo: Japan Publications, 1978
Kushi, Aveline with Alex Jack, *Aveline Kushi's Complete Guide to Macrobiotic Cooking for Health, Happiness and Peace*, Warner Publishing Co., 1984
Kushi, Aveline with Wendy Esko, *The Changing Seasons Macrobiotic Cookbook*, Wayne, NJ, Avery Publishing Group, 1984
Ohsawa, Lima, *Macrobiotic Cuisine*, Tokyo: Japan Publications, 1984

Other Macrotiotic or Related Books

Aihara, Herman, *Basic Macrobiotics* Tokyo, Japan Publications, 1985
Brown, Virginia with Susan Stayman, *Macrobiotic Miracle: How a Vermont Family Overcame Cancer*, Tokyo, Japan Publications, 1985
Dufty, William, *Sugar Blues*, New York, Warner, 1975
East West Journal (Periodical), Brookline, MA
Heidenry, Carolyn, *An Introduction to Macrobiotics: A Beginner's Guide to the Natural Way of Health*, Florence, Italy, Aladdin Press, 1984
Heidenry, Carolyn, *Making the Transition to a Macrobiotic Diet*, Florence, Italy, Aladdin Press, 1984
Heidenry, Carolyn, *Crossroads: America's Future—Decline or Ascent*, Florence Italy, Aladdin Press, 1984
Heidenry, Carolyn, *Yin Yang Coloring Book for Children*, Florence, Italy, Aladdin Press, 1984
Ineson, Rev. John, *The Way of Life: Macrobiotics and the Spirit of Christianity*, Tokyo, Japan Publications, 1985

Kohler, Jean and Mary Alice, *Healing Miracles from Macrobiotics*, West Nyack, NY, Parker, 1979

Kotzsch, Ronald E., Ph. D., *Macrobiotics: Yesterday and Today*, Tokyo, Japan Publications, 1985

Kushi, Aveline, *Lessons of Day and Night*, Wayne, NJ, Avery Publishing Group, 1984

Kushi, Aveline with Wendy Esko, *Growing Up Naturally: Macrobiotic Cooking for Healthy Children*, Tokyo, Japan Publications, 1985

Kushi, Aveline and Michio, *Macrobiotic Pregnancy and Care of the Newborn*, Tokyo, Japan Publications, 1984

Kushi, Aveline and Michio with Edward and Wendy Esko, *Macrobiotic Childcare and Family Health*, Tokyo, Japan Publications, 1985

Kushi, Michio, *The Book of Macrobiotics*, Tokyo, Japan Publications, 1977

Kushi, Michio, *Cancer and Heart Disease: The Macrobiotic Approach to Degenerative Disorders* (Revised edition), Tokyo, Japan Publications, 1985

Kushi, Michio, *Natural Healing Through Macrobiotics*, Tokyo, Japan Publications, 1978

Kushi, Michio, *The Era of Humanity*, Brookline, MA, East West Journal, 1980

Kushi, Michio, *How to See Your Health: The Book of Oriental Diagnosis*, Tokyo, Japan Publications, 1980

Kushi, Michio, *Your Face Never Lies*, Wayne, NJ, The Avery Publishing Group, 1983

Kushi, Michio, *The Book of Dō-In: Exercise for Physical and Spiritual Development*, Tokyo, Japan Publications, 1979

Kushi, Michio and the East West Foundation, *The Macrobiotic Approach to Cancer*, Wayne, NJ, The Avery Publishing Group, 1982

Kushi, Michio with Alex Jack, *The Cancer Prevention Diet*, NY, St. Martin's Press, 1983

Kushi, Michio with Alex Jack, *Eating to Your Heart's Content: The Natural Way to Relieve and Prevent Heart Attack, Stroke, and High Blood Pressure*, NY, St. Martin's Press, 1985

Kushi, Michio with Marc Van Cauwenberghe, *Macrobiotic Home Remedies*, Tokyo, Japan Publications, 1985

Mendelsohn, Robert, S., M.D., *Confessions of a Medical Heretic*, NY, Warner, 1979

Mendelsohn, Robert S., M.D., *Male Practice*, Chicago, Contemporary Books 1980

Nussbaum, Elaine, *Recovery: From Cancer to Health Through Macrobiotics*, Tokyo, Japan Publications, 1985

Ohsawa, George, *Cancer and the Philosophy of the Far East*, Oroville, CA, George Ohsawa Macrobiotic Foundation, 1971

Ohsawa, George and Dufty, William, *You Are All Sanpaku*, NY, University Books, 1965

Sattilaro, Anthony, M.D. with Tom Monte, *Recalled by Life: The Story of My Recovery from Cancer*, Boston, Houghton-Mifflin, 1982

Tara, William, *Macrobiotics and Human Behavior*, Tokyo, Japan Publications, 1985

Index